Ellenora and Kittie Allen
March 30, 1899 —

Mrs. J. G. Hunter

SILAS MARNER

George Eliot

GEORGE ELIOT'S

SILAS MARNER

EDITED
WITH INTRODUCTION AND NOTES

BY

R. ADELAIDE WITHAM, B.A.

TEACHER OF ENGLISH IN LATIN SCHOOL, SOMERVILLE, MASS.

BOSTON, U.S.A.
GINN & COMPANY, PUBLISHERS
The Athenæum Press
1898

PREFACE.

THE following plan is designed to meet the requirements of the Committee of Ten; namely, "The student shall be made familiar with the subject-matter, form, and structure of the book; shall be able to answer simple questions on the life of the author and the literary period in which he lived; and shall be taught to state with clear and accurate expression his own independent criticism of the author's work." This is the bare working rule laid down by the conference, but in addition to this scheme there are certain other aims indispensable to class-room work.

Of these aims, the plan here presented points *first* to the simple object, pleasure. "As good kill a man as kill a good book." Reading even a good book from a sense of duty only is of little benefit, and may do as much harm as the reading of literary refuse; for an aversion to the good is already a leaning toward the evil. Students will read what they love, and they must be taught to love that which is worth their admiration. If they feel that the reading of this book is a matter of pleasure as well as of discipline, the drudgery of study is already minimized. Nor need the pleasure in this instance be confined to the reading of *Silas Marner* only. Comparisons with the works of Dickens, Thackeray, and others will prove a stimulus to outside reading and open up an unknown field of pleasure.

The *second* aim is to procure for classes a solid amount of the old Bible "understanding." "With all thy getting, get understanding." For this specific object, biographical out-line, bibliographies, chronological table, notes, and questions are introduced.

The *third* aim is to send each student away from the class-room fully able to teach the day's lesson to some one else. A class should not feel that the teacher has certain mysterious reasons for his method of work, or that questions are to be asked and answered simply for his own satisfaction. A teacher's method belongs as much to his class as to himself. A pupil should be taught through this one book to read all books understandingly. This point cannot be too strenuously emphasized by the teacher. A plan which sees the end from the beginning, and which in itself is a *working model*, ought to give pupils the ability of extracting from any book all that is good and personally helpful.

Fourth. Students are sometimes appalled at the boldness of criticising the great writers of the world. This false humility is a tremendous hindrance to class work. There are certain rules and principles governing all literary work. A student possessing these may be master in a sense of even a George Eliot. He who has not the creative, can cultivate the critical faculty, and the man who is able to judge a book with appreciation is second only to its author.

Fifth. No notes have been made on any expression that can be found in a good dictionary or encyclopedia ; and for a similar reason a written sketch of the life of the author has been omitted, and in its place a comprehensive outline substituted. The bibliography is not taken at random from Poole's *Index*, but contains only such articles as have been proved useful by actual class work. First sources of informa-tion belong as much to the pupil as to the teacher ; the middle-man always detracts something from the original value. It is important that the class should have a feeling of ownership of all that has been written about George

Eliot. No student must think that all he needs to know of *Silas Marner* is contained in these two covers, but should explore for himself the broader fields of knowledge about this one little book.

Finally, the object which pervades the whole work is to touch the heart of the student with the great heart of George Eliot. Young people in high schools and academies have had life experiences of their own, and are quick to recognize sympathetic comprehension on the part of a writer. Let them read the life of George Eliot, feel the strength of her character, her wonderful sympathy, her comprehension of other lives, and she becomes at once a friend to them. The reading of *Silas Marner* will then be a preparation not only for college, but, in a measure, for life. The spiritual tragedy in the story of Silas Marner is real enough to enlist the interest of each of us. It lays bare the workings of the heart, its motives and struggles. There is no one of us to whom the problem of Silas's weakness may not be a warning; the study of the character that proved his salvation is for us all a moral and spiritual stimulus. As George Eliot said herself, "My books are written out of my deepest belief, and as well as I can for the great public; and every strong, sincere word will find its mark in that public."

BIBLIOGRAPHIES.

⸺◦◦⸘⸘◦◦⸺

LIFE OF GEORGE ELIOT.

Life of George Eliot, by John Walter Cross (1884).

Portrait of George Eliot, by F. W. Meyers. *Century*, Nov. 1881.

Life of George Eliot, by Henry James, Jr. *Atlantic*, May, 1885.

Life of George Eliot, by Frederic Harrison. *Fortnightly Review*, May, 1885.

Life of George Eliot, by Mathilde Blind. *Famous Women Series*.

George Eliot's County, by Rose Kingsley. *Century*, July, 1885. Mill on the Floss. 1st half.

Life, Writings, and Philosophy, by Cooke.

CRITICISMS ON NOVELS.

George Eliot, by Leslie Stephen. Half Hours in a Library.

The English Novel and Principles of its Development, by Sidney Lanier.

Essays in Literary Criticism, by R. H. Hutton.

George Eliot's Children, by Annie Matheson. Macmillan's, Oct. 1882.

CRITICISMS ON POETRY.

Poems of George Eliot, by W. D. Howells. *Atlantic*, July, 1874.

Poems of George Eliot, by Henry James. *North American Review*, Oct. 1874.

English Poetesses, by Eric Robertson. 1883.

LIFE OF GEORGE ELIOT.

1819–1880.

NAMES.

Mary Ann (Marian) Evans.
Mrs. George Henry Lewes.
Mrs. John Walter Cross.
Nom de plume, George Eliot.

I. Birth and Parents.

1. *Birth.*

> "George IV did not come to the throne till January, 1820, so that George Eliot was born in the reign of George III. Waterloo was not yet an affair five years old. Byron had four years and Goethe had thirteen years still to live. The last of Miss Austen's novels had been published only eighteen months and the first of the *Waverleys* only six years before. Thackeray and Dickens were boys at school, and George Sand a girl of fifteen." [1]

2. *Father* (furnished model for Adam Bede and Caleb Garth).

> "In all respects I considered him a man so much to my honor that the mention of my relationship to him was likely to secure me regard."

3. *Mother* (furnished model for Mrs. Poyser; and her family, the model for the Dodsons).

> "Hers was an affectionate, warm-hearted nature, and her children on whom she cast the benediction of her gaze were warmly attached to her."

---

[1] The quotations are from Cross's "Life," or George Eliot's own letters. It is intended that the pupil shall fill out the topics himself.

II. Childhood.

Read poem, "Brother and Sister." Relations with brother portrayed in Maggie and Tom Tulliver.

> "An old-fashioned child, already living in a world of her own imagination, impressible to the finger-tips, and willing to give my views on any subject."

> "When I was a child I could not be satisfied with the things around me; I was constantly living in a world of my own creation, and was quite contented to have no companions that I might be left to my own musings and imagine scenes in which I was the chief actress."

III. Education.

> "There was nothing of the infant phenomenon about George Eliot."

> "Books became a passion with the child, and she read everything that she could lay hands on." See motto to ch. 57 of "Middlemarch."

IV. Relations with Father.

(Early.) Picture of life at Griff House.

> "The powerful, middle-aged man with the strongly-marked features sits in his deep leather-covered armchair at the right hand of the ruddy fireplace, with the head of 'the little wench' between his knees. The child pores over a book that she wishes her father to explain to her. Her rebellious hair is all over her eyes, much vexing the pale, energetic mother. The father is already very proud of the astonishing and growing intelligence of his little girl. From a very early age he has been in the habit of taking her with him in his drives about the neighborhood, standing between her father's knees as he drove leisurely, so that she has drunk in knowledge of the country and of country folk at all her pores."

(Late.) "What shall I be without my father? It will seem as if part of my moral nature were gone."

V. First Journey to Continent.

Upon death of father. Time spent at Geneva.

> "Development of artistic and emotional side of nature; deepening of love for England."

VI. Connection with Westminster Review.

Editorial connection with greatest contemporary writers; beginning of intimacy with Mr. Lewes.

VII. Union with Mr. Lewes.

> "If there is any one action or relation of my life which is, and always has been, profoundly serious, it is my relation with Mr. Lewes." Read letter to Mrs. Bray, Sept. 1885. — Cross's "Life," ch. 5.

1. Travels abroad.

   "Happy working days at Berlin, Munich, Dresden, Florence, Naples, Rome, with all the music, poetry, and art of the Old World at my hand."

2. Scenes from Clerical Life.

   "Such humor, pathos, vivid presentation, and nice observation have not been exhibited since the 'Vicar of Wakefield.'"

   "I ordered copies sent to Dickens, Thackeray, Tennyson, Ruskin." — From Blackwood's Letter.

VIII. Publication of Adam Bede.

Thomas Carlyle to Mr. Blackwood :

   "The book you forwarded is a human book, written out of the heart of a live *man*, and not merely out of the brain of an author."

Mrs. Jane Welsh Carlyle :

   "When I finished it, I found myself in charity with the whole human race."

Incident of Liggins. — Cross's "Life," ch. 8.

IX. Period of Greatest Literary Activity.

1858–1878.

Although critics differ, "Middlemarch" is usually considered the strongest of the novels in conception and presentation. "Adam Bede" and "Mill on the Floss" probably are equally popular.

X. Marriage with Mr. Cross.

George Eliot's letters are singularly reserved and few at the time of Mr. Lewes's death and her almost immediate marriage with Mr. Cross. The key to the mystery is in a very early letter, in which she says, "It is absolutely necessary to my nature that I should be all in all to some one who is all in all to me."

XI. Social Life.

Read description of her receptions.   Cross's "Life," ch. 18.
                                          Blind's "Life."

XII. Death.

Wonderful mental activity to end.
Read "Oh, May I Join the Choir Invisible!"

I. PLACE IN THE LITERATURE OF THE WORLD.

The English Novel and the Principle of its Development, by Sidney Lanier.

Half Hours in a Library, by Leslie Stephen.
Essays in Literary Criticism, by R. H. Hutton.

II. RELATION TO OTHER WRITERS.

Thackeray. *Atlantic*, Feb. 1883.
Carlyle. *Independent*, Mar. 1883 (Stopford Brooke).
Hawthorne. *North British*, Nov. 1860. " He is a great favorite of mine."
Emerson. *Century*, Feb. 1882. " The first *man* I have ever seen."

III. SOME CONTEMPORARIES.

1. ENGLISH LITERATURE.

Dickens	Macaulay
Thackeray	Spencer
Lewes	Carlyle
Robert Browning	Darwin
Elizabeth B. Browning	Tennyson
Ruskin	Froude

Matthew Arnold

2. AMERICAN LITERATURE.

Whittier	Holmes
Hawthorne	Lowell
Longfellow	Howells
Emerson	James

IV. WORKS.

NOVELS IN ORDER OF PUBLICATION.

1. Scenes from Clerical Life. 1857.
2. Adam Bede. (Established fame.) 1859.
3. Mill on Floss. 1860.
4. Silas Marner. (To be read.) 1861.
5. Romola. 1863. (" I came out from this an old woman.")
6. Felix Holt. 1866.
7. Middlemarch. 1872.
8. Daniel Deronda. 1876.
9. Theophrastus Such. 1879.

POETRY.

(To be read.)

Spanish Gypsy.

Selections:

    a. " The time is great, and greater no man's trust." Bk. I.
    b. " 'T is daylight still." Bk. I.
    c. " So soft a night was never made for sleep." Bk. I.
    d. Pablo's Song: " The world is great." Bk. II.
    e. Fedelma's Prayer: " Father, my soul is weak." Bk. III.

Legend of Jubal.

How Lisa Loved the King.

Stradivarius.

TRANSLATIONS.

Strauss's " Life of Jesus."
Feuerbach's " Essence of Christianity."

V. GEORGE ELIOT'S TREATMENT OF CHARACTER.

The history of the growth of the English novel is the history of the growth of interest in man for man's sake. In 1859 Mr. Blackwood received two letters in acknowledgment of a book which he had sent to Thomas Carlyle. The first said, "The book you forwarded is a *human* book, written out of the heart of a live man, and not merely out of the brain of an author." The second, from Mrs. Carlyle, said, "When I finished it, I found myself in charity with the whole human race." The book was *Adam Bede;* the writer not a "live man," but a thinking woman; and the two criticisms mark the great particular in which that book and all George Eliot's subsequent works differ from those of the novelists before her.

She, too, had her "literary microscope" which she used as scientifically, coolly, and critically as her predecessors, but her observations were tinged with her own personal equation of profound sympathy and keen understanding of all human life. The early novelists had studied the life of man analytically and justly, too, perhaps; but the results had usually been to make their characters monsters of vice or, what was equally unnatural, monuments of virtues. Dickens and Thackeray, to be sure, painted men as they were; but they spent all their art in bringing out that one aspect of human nature which they saw most prominent in a man to the destruction of absolute truthfulness of the whole nature of man. As Becky Sharpe will always be a synonym for ambitious cunning; Amelia Sedley for childish constancy; Mr. Micawber for eternal springing hope; and Silas Wegg for inspired poetry; so we might go on through the whole rôle. But no character in George Eliot's novels can be described by one word or phrase.

Step by step, consistently with carefully stated premises, she develops her characters, living with them and feeling their struggles and failures keenly. So intense did this absorption in *Mill on the Floss* become that its completion was followed by weeks of utter physical and mental prostration. Can we imagine Dickens or Thackeray suffering as they wrote? Thackeray does say somewhere that Becky Sharpe after awhile became too much even for him, but we can fancy his amusement at the chase she was leading him. In *Janet's Repentance* George Eliot says, "Surely the only true knowledge of our fellow-man is that which enables us to feel with him, which gives us a fine ear for the heart pulses that are beating under the mere clothes of circumstance and opinion. Our subtlest analysis of people must miss the essential truth unless it be lighted by the love which sees in all forms of human thought and work, the life and death struggle of human beings." It was to call forth tolerant judgment and pity between man and man, to arouse sympathy for the constant sacrifice of individuals and the difficulty of the adjustment of the human will to destiny, that her whole genius was spent.

Does it seem as if this ruling passion of sympathy would lead George Eliot to disregard scientific truths of life development, we have only to examine her works. She was too scientific herself, too well versed in all aspects of the scientific awakening of her own time, to let any other interest overbalance truth itself. It is easy to see the characteristic situation of all her novels. As Sidney Lanier puts it, "It is that of a hungering life, at first balked by adverse circumstances, wasting itself on something unworthy — often from pure ignorance as to where anything nobler is to be found — but after struggling, finally finding better and larger life and love." This, in varying degree, is the position of *Romola*, *Dorothea*, *Adam Bede*, *Daniel Deronda*, and *Silas Marner*. In each case, the environment and inherited tendencies of the character are given, and not once is the development inconsistent with them. Sometimes the miserliness of Marner may seem to us forced, but we may be sure that it is because we do not see as far beneath the surface as does George Eliot. If the crisis in the lives of the Cass brothers seems unnatural, we must only remind ourselves of what George Eliot never forgot, namely, that criminal impulses may be felt by natures which we could hardly characterize as criminal; that the conduct of a man is not determined at a crisis by reflection alone, but also by the necessities of his lot in life; and that no man stands alone to act for himself, but has a share in the lives of his fellow creatures which he cannot escape. Each life, to her, must be worked out with more or less tragedy; none could ever be wholly free from it.

But she would not have allowed that the same determinism governs the stones of the road and the lives of men. She says of Darwin's *Origin of Species:* "To me the development theory and all other explanations of the process by which things came to be are as nothing compared to the mystery of life which lies under them." And again she writes, "Pain and relief, love and sorrow, have their peculiar histories which make an experience and knowledge over and above the swing of atoms." It is the mystery and dignity of life, which she makes us reverence as she does, that is the ideal element in her realistic work. People may say her books are fatalistic, but they are no more fatal than life itself. She wept once when Mr. Cross told her that her books were essentially sad, but it was from the consciousness that life itself was sad and she had drawn its truth. But hers is the strong element of sympathy and pity for life that keeps the sadness from becoming morbidness. Hope has its own strong salutary part in her work; she always holds up the possibility of moral greatness, and her men and women who struggle most bravely succeed. So, although her philosophy of life is one of necessity; yet to her all human nature is capable of resolving upon a high ideal and attaining it. We feel from the premises what will be the lives of Godfrey Cass and Silas Marner, and the story of the strife brings in the ideal element of the work and makes the story an unpreached sermon, which "he who runs may read."

When some one asked George Eliot if she had ever heard a sermon preached by the aunt from whom she drew the picture of Dinah Morris, she answered, "No; the words of the sermon I made Dinah preach came to me as tears come, because our hearts are full and we cannot keep them back. My books are deeply serious things to me and come out of all the painful discipline and most hardly learned lessons of my life." That was the secret of her genius. Life was more to her than what a mere observer of man's experience with it could see with all his keenness and skill. She wrote with her heart and from her heart, and if the reader feels her wonderful understanding and sympathy, a book like *Silas Marner* may become a new and rich experience to him. It was as she said, "The great, great facts of life have struggled to find a voice through me." And with her conception of the real mystery of life she added, "And have been able to speak only brokenly." But the hearts of her world of readers can judge of that better than she herself.

SILAS MARNER,

THE WEAVER OF RAVELOE.

———◦◦∘◦——

PART I.

———

CHAPTER I.

IN the days when the spinning wheels hummed busily in the farmhouses — and even great ladies, clothed in silk and thread-lace, had their toy spinning wheels of polished oak — there might be seen, in districts far away among the lanes or deep in the bosom of the hills, certain pallid, undersized men, who, by the side of the brawny country folk, looked like the remnants of a disinherited race. The shepherd's dog barked fiercely when one of these alien-looking men appeared on the upland, dark against the early winter sunset; for what dog likes a figure bent under a heavy bag? — and these pale men rarely stirred abroad without that mysterious burden. The shepherd himself, though he had good reason to believe that the bag held nothing but flaxen thread, or else the long rolls of strong linen spun from that thread, was not quite sure that this trade of weaving, indispensable though it was, could be carried on entirely without the help of the Evil One. In that far-off time superstition clung easily round every person or thing that was at all unwonted, or even intermittent and occasional merely, 20 like the visits of the peddler or the knife-grinder. No one knew where wandering men had their homes or their origin ; and how was a man to be explained unless you at least knew somebody who knew his father and mother ? To the peasants of old times, the world outside their own direct experience was a region of vagueness and mystery ; to their untraveled thought a state of wandering was a conception as dim as the winter life of the swallows that came back with the spring ; and even a settler, if he came from distant parts, hardly ever ceased to be viewed with a remnant of distrust, which would have prevented any surprise if a long course of inoffensive conduct on his part had ended in the commission of a crime, especially if he had any reputation for knowledge or showed any skill in handicraft. All cleverness, whether in the rapid use of that difficult instrument the tongue, or in some other art unfamiliar to villagers, was in itself suspicious; honest folk, born and bred in a visible manner, were mostly not over wise or clever — at least, not beyond such a matter as knowing the signs of the weather; and the process by which rapidity and dexterity of any kind were acquired was so wholly hidden that they partook of the nature of conjuring. In this way it came to pass that those scattered linen weavers — emigrants from the town into the country — were to the last regarded as aliens by their rustic neighbors, and usually contracted the eccentric habits which belong to a state of loneliness.

In the early years of this century, such a linen weaver, named Silas Marner, worked at his vocation in a stone cottage that stood among the nutty hedgerows near the village of Raveloe, and not far from the edge of a deserted stone pit. The questionable sound of Silas's loom, so unlike the natural cheerful trotting of the winnowing machine or the simpler rhythm of the flail, had a half-

fearful fascination for the Raveloe boys, who would often
leave off their nutting or birds'-nesting to peep in at the
window of the stone cottage, counterbalancing a certain
awe at the mysterious action of the loom, by a pleasant
sense of scornful superiority, drawn from the mockery 5
of its alternating noises, along with the bent, tread-mill
attitude of the weaver. But sometimes it happened that
Marner, pausing to adjust an irregularity in his thread,
became aware of the small scoundrels, and, though chary
of his time, he liked their intrusion so ill that he would 10
descend from his loom, and, opening the door, would fix
on them a gaze that was always enough to make them
take to their legs in terror. For how was it possible to
believe that those large brown protuberant eyes in Silas
Marner's pale face really saw nothing very distinctly that 15
was not close to them, and not rather that their dreadful
stare could dart cramp, or rickets, or a wry mouth at any
boy who happened to be in the rear? They had, perhaps,
heard their fathers and mothers hint that Silas Marner
could cure folks' rheumatism if he had a mind, and add, 20
still more darkly, that if you could only speak the devil
fair enough, he might save you the cost of the doctor.
Such strange, lingering echoes of the old demon-worship
might perhaps even now be caught by the diligent listener
among the gray-haired peasantry ; for the rude mind with 25
difficulty associates the ideas of power and benignity. A
shadowy conception of power that by much persuasion
can be induced to refrain from inflicting harm is the
shape most easily taken by the sense of the Invisible in
the minds of men who have always been pressed close 30
by primitive wants, and to whom a life of hard toil has
never been illuminated by any enthusiastic religious faith.
To them pain and mishap present a far wider range of
possibilities than gladness and enjoyment ; their imagi-

nation is almost barren of the images that feed desire and
hope, but is all overgrown by recollections that are a
perpetual pasture to fear. " Is there anything you can
fancy that you would like to eat ? " I once said to an old
5 laboring man, who was in his last illness, and who had
refused all the food his wife had offered him. " No," he
answered, " I 've never been used to nothing but common
victual, and I can't eat that." Experience had bred no
fancies in him that could raise the phantasm of appetite.
10   And Raveloe was a village where many of the old
echoes lingered, undrowned by new voices. Not that it
was one of those barren parishes lying on the outskirts
of civilization, inhabited by meager sheep and thinly
scattered shepherds : on the contrary, it lay in the rich
15 central plain of what we are pleased to call Merry England, and held farms which, speaking from a spiritual
point of view, paid highly-desirable tithes. But it was
nestled in a snug, well-wooded hollow, quite an hour's
journey on horseback from any turnpike, where it was
20 never reached by the vibrations of the coach-horn, or of
public opinion. It was an important-looking village,
with a fine old church and large churchyard in the heart
of it, and two or three large brick-and-stone homesteads,
with well-walled orchards and ornamental weathercocks,
25 standing close upon the road, and lifting more imposing
fronts than the rectory, which peeped from among the
trees on the other side of the churchyard : — a village
which showed at once the summits of its social life, and
told the practiced eye that there was no great park and
30 manor-house in the vicinity, but that there were several
chiefs in Raveloe who could farm badly quite at their
ease, drawing enough money from their bad farming, in
those war times, to live in a rollicking fashion, and keep
a jolly Christmas, Whitsun, and Easter tide.

It was fifteen years since Silas Marner had first come to Raveloe ; he was then simply a pallid young man, with prominent, short-sighted brown eyes, whose appearance would have had nothing strange for people of average culture and experience, but for the villagers near whom he had come to settle it had mysterious peculiarities, which corresponded with the exceptional nature of his occupation and his advent from an unknown region called "North'ard." So had his way of life : he invited no comer to step across his door-sill, and he never strolled into the village to drink a pint at the Rainbow or to gossip at the wheelwright's ; he sought no man or woman, save for the purposes of his calling, or in order to supply himself with necessaries ; and it was soon clear to the Raveloe lasses that he would never urge one of them to accept him against her will — quite as if he had heard them declare that they would never marry a dead man come to life again. This view of Marner's personality was not without another ground than his pale face and unexampled eyes ; for Jem Rodney, the mole catcher, averred that one evening as he was returning homeward he saw Silas Marner leaning against a stile with a heavy bag on his back, instead of resting the bag on the stile, as a man in his senses would have done ; and that, on coming up to him, he saw that Marner's eyes were set like a dead man's, and he spoke to him, and shook him, and his limbs were stiff, and his hands clutched the bag as if they 'd been made of iron ; but just as he had made up his mind that the weaver was dead, he came all right again, like, as you might say, in the winking of an eye, and said "Good-night," and walked off. All this Jem swore he had seen, more by token that it was the very day he had been mole catching on Squire Cass's land, down by the old saw-pit. Some said Marner must have

been in a "fit," a word which seemed to explain things
otherwise incredible ; but the argumentative Mr. Macey,
clerk of the parish, shook his head, and asked if anybody
was ever known to go off in a fit and not fall down.   A
5 fit was a stroke, was n't it ? and it was in the nature of a
stroke to partly take away the use of a man's limbs and
throw him on the parish, if he 'd got no children to look
to.   No, no; it was no stroke that would let a man stand
on his legs, like a horse between the shafts, and then
10 walk off as soon as you can say " Gee ! "   But there
might be such a thing as a man's soul being loose from
his body, and going out and in, like a bird out of its nest
and back ; and that was how folks got over-wise, for they
went to school in this shell-less state to those who could
15 teach them more than their neighbors could learn with
their five senses and the parson.   And where did Master
Marner get his knowledge of herbs from — and charms,
too, if he liked to give them away ?   Jem Rodney's story
was no more than what might have been expected by
20 anybody who had seen how Marner had cured Sally
Oates, and made her sleep like a baby, when her heart
had been beating enough to burst her body for two
months and more, while she had been under the doctor's
care.   He might cure more folks if he would; but he
25 was worth speaking fair, if it was only to keep him from
doing you a mischief.

   It was partly to this vague fear that Marner was in-
debted for protecting him from the persecution that his
singularities might have drawn upon him, but still more
30 to the fact that, the old linen weaver in the neighboring
parish of Tarley being dead, his handicraft made him a
highly welcome settler to the richer housewives of the
district, and even to the more provident cottagers, who
had their little stock of yarn at the year's end.   Their

sense of his usefulness would have counteracted any repugnance or suspicion which was not confirmed by a deficiency in the quality or the tale of the cloth he wove for them. And the years had rolled on without producing any change in the impressions of the neighbors concerning Marner, except the change from novelty to habit. At the end of fifteen years the Raveloe men said just the same things about Silas Marner as at the beginning; they did not say them quite so often, but they believed them much more strongly when they did say them. There was only one important addition which the years had brought : it was that Master Marner had laid by a fine sight of money somewhere, and that he could buy up "bigger men" than himself.

But while opinion concerning him had remained nearly stationary, and his daily habits had presented scarcely any visible change, Marner's inward life had been a history and a metamorphosis, as that of every fervid nature must be when it has fled or been condemned to solitude. His life before he came to Raveloe had been filled with the movement, the mental activity, and the close fellowship, which, in that day as in this, marked the life of an artisan early incorporated in a narrow religious sect, where the poorest layman has the chance of distinguishing himself by gifts of speech, and has, at the very least, the weight of a silent voter in the government of his community. Marner was highly thought of in that little hidden world, known to itself as the church assembling in Lantern Yard ; he was believed to be a young man of exemplary life and ardent faith, and a peculiar interest had been centered in him ever since he had fallen, at a prayer meeting, into a mysterious rigidity and suspension of consciousness, which, lasting for an hour or more, had been mistaken for death. To have sought a medical

explanation for this phenomenon would have been held
by Silas himself, as well as by his minister and fellow-
members, a willful self-exclusion from the spiritual significance that might lie therein. Silas was evidently a
5 brother selected for a peculiar discipline ; and though the
effort to interpret this discipline was discouraged by the
absence, on his part, of any spiritual vision during his
outward trance, yet it was believed by himself and others
that its effect was seen in an accession of light and fervor.
10 A less truthful man than he might have been tempted
into the subsequent creation of a vision in the form of
resurgent memory ; a less sane man might have believed
in such a creation ; but Silas was both sane and honest,
though, as with many honest and fervent men, culture had
15 not defined any channels for his sense of mystery, and so
it spread itself over the proper pathway of inquiry and
knowledge. He had inherited from his mother some
acquaintance with medicinal herbs and their preparation,
— a little store of wisdom which she had imparted to him
20 as a solemn bequest, — but of late years he had had
doubts about the lawfulness of applying this knowledge,
believing that herbs could have no efficacy without prayer,
and that prayer might suffice without herbs ; so that his
inherited delight to wander through the fields in search
25 of foxglove and dandelion and coltsfoot began to wear
to him the character of a temptation.

Among the members of his church there was one
young man, a little older than himself, with whom he
had long lived in such close friendship that it was the
30 custom of their Lantern Yard brethren to call them David
and Jonathan. The real name of the friend was William
Dane, and he, too, was regarded as a shining instance of
youthful piety, though somewhat given to over-severity
towards weaker brethren, and to be so dazzled by his

own light as to hold himself wiser than his teachers. But, whatever blemishes others might discern in William, to his friend's mind he was faultless; for Marner had one of those impressible, self-doubting natures which, at an inexperienced age, admire imperativeness and lean 5 on contradiction. The expression of trusting simplicity in Marner's face, heightened by that absence of special observation, that defenseless, deer-like gaze which belongs to large, prominent eyes, was strongly contrasted by the self-complacent suppression of inward triumph that 10 lurked in the narrow, slanting eyes and compressed lips of William Dane. One of the most frequent topics of conversation between the two friends was Assurance of Salvation: Silas confessed that he could never arrive at anything higher than hope mingled with fear, and 15 listened with longing wonder when William declared that he had possessed unshaken assurance ever since, in the period of his conversion, he had dreamed that he saw the words " calling and election sure " standing by themselves on a white page in the open Bible. Such 20 colloquies have occupied many a pair of pale-faced weavers, whose unnurtured souls have been like young winged things, fluttering forsaken in the twilight.

It had seemed to the unsuspecting Silas that the friendship had suffered no chill even from his forma- 25 tion of another attachment of a closer kind. For some months he had been engaged to a young servant woman, waiting only for a little increase to their mutual savings in order to their marriage; and it was a great delight to him that Sarah did not object to William's occasional 30 presence in their Sunday interviews. It was at this point in their history that Silas's cataleptic fit occurred during the prayer meeting; and amidst the various queries and expressions of interest addressed to him

by his fellow-members, William's suggestion alone jarred
with the general sympathy towards a brother thus singled
out for special dealings. He observed that, to him, this
trance looked more like a visitation of Satan than a proof
5 of divine favor, and exhorted his friend to see that he hid
no accursed thing within his soul. Silas, feeling bound
to accept rebuke and admonition as a brotherly office,
felt no resentment, but only pain, at his friend's doubts
concerning him; and to this was soon added some
10 anxiety at the perception that Sarah's manner towards
him began to exhibit a strange fluctuation between an
effort at an increased manifestation of regard and invol-
untary signs of shrinking and dislike. He asked her if
she wished to break off their engagement; but she denied
15 this. Their engagement was known to the church, and
had been recognized in the prayer meetings; it could
not be broken off without strict investigation, and Sarah
could render no reason that would be sanctioned by
the feeling of the community. At this time the senior
20 deacon was taken dangerously ill, and, being a childless
widower, he was tended night and day by some of the
younger brethren or sisters. Silas frequently took his
turn in the night watching with William, the one relieving
the other at two in the morning. The old man, contrary
25 to expectation, seemed to be on the way to recovery,
when, one night, Silas, sitting up by his bedside, observed
that his usual audible breathing had ceased. The candle
was burning low, and he had to lift it to see the patient's
face. distinctly. Examination convinced him that the
30 deacon was dead—had been dead some time, for the limbs
were rigid. Silas asked himself if he had been asleep, and
looked at the clock : it was already four in the morning.
How was it that William had not come? In much anxiety,
he went to seek for help, and soon there were several friends

assembled in the house, the minister among them, while
Silas went away to his work, wishing he could have met
William to know the reason of his non-appearance.   But
at six o'clock, as he was thinking of going to seek his
friend, William came, and with him the minister.   They   5
came to summon him to Lantern Yard, to meet the
church members there; and to his inquiry concerning
the cause of the summons the only reply was, "You will
hear."   Nothing further was said until Silas was seated
in the vestry, in front of the minister, with the eyes   10
of those who to him represented God's people fixed
solemnly upon him.   Then the minister, taking out a
pocket knife, showed it to Silas, and asked him if he
knew where he had left that knife.   Silas said he did
not know that he had left it anywhere out of his own   15
pocket; but he was trembling at this strange interroga-
tion.   He was then exhorted not to hide his sin, but to
confess and repent.   The knife had been found in the
bureau by the departed deacon's bedside—found in the
place where the little bag of church money had lain,   20
which the minister himself had seen the day before.
Some hand had removed that bag; and whose hand
could it be, if not that of the man to whom the knife
belonged?   For some time Silas was mute with astonishment; then he said, "God will clear me; I know   25
nothing about the knife being there or the money being
gone.   Search me and my dwelling; you will find nothing
but three pound five of my own savings, which William
Dane knows I have had these six months."   At this
William groaned, but the minister said, "The proof is   30
heavy against you, Brother Marner.   The money was
taken in the night last past, and no man was with our
departed brother but you, for William Dane declares to
us that he was hindered by sudden sickness from going

to take his place as usual, and you yourself said that he had not come; and, moreover, you neglected the dead body."

"I must have slept," said Silas. Then, after a pause, he added, "Or I must have had another visitation like that which you have all seen me under, so that the thief must have come and gone while I was not in the body, but out of the body. But, I say again, search me and my dwelling, for I have been nowhere else."

The search was made, and it ended — in William Dane's finding the well-known bag, empty, tucked behind the chest of drawers in Silas's chamber! On this William exhorted his friend to confess and not to hide his sin any longer. Silas turned a look of keen reproach on him, and said, "William, for nine years that we have gone in and out together, have you ever known me tell a lie? But God will clear me."

"Brother," said William, "how do I know what you may have done in the secret chambers of your heart to give Satan an advantage over you?"

Silas was still looking at his friend. Suddenly a deep flush came over his face, and he was about to speak impetuously when he seemed checked again by some inward shock that sent the flush back and made him tremble. But at last he spoke feebly, looking at William:

"I remember now — the knife wasn't in my pocket."

William said, "I know nothing of what you mean." The other persons present, however, began to inquire where Silas meant to say that the knife was, but he would give no further explanation. He only said, "I am sore stricken; I can say nothing. God will clear me."

On their return to the vestry there was further deliberation. Any resort to legal measures for ascertaining the culprit was contrary to the principles of the church in

Lantern Yard, according to which prosecution was for-
bidden to Christians, even had the case held less scandal
to the community.   But the members were bound to take
other measures for finding out the truth, and they resolved
on praying and drawing lots.   This resolution can be a   5
ground of surprise only to those who are unacquainted
with that obscure religious life which has gone on in the
alleys of our towns.   Silas knelt with his brethren, relying
on his own innocence being certified by immediate divine
interference, but feeling that there was sorrow and mourn-   10
ing behind for him even then — that his trust in man had
been cruelly bruised.   *The lots declared that Silas Marner
was guilty.*   He was solemnly suspended from church
membership, and called upon to render up the stolen
money; only on confession, as the sign of repentance,   15
could he be received once more within the folds of the
church.   Marner listened in silence.   At last, when every
one rose to depart, he went towards William Dane and
said, in a voice shaken by agitation :

"The last time I remember using my knife was when   20
I took it out to cut a strap for you.   I don't remember
putting it in my pocket again.   *You* stole the money, and
you have woven a plot to lay the sin at my door.   But
you may prosper, for all that ; there is no just God that
governs the earth righteously, but a God of lies, that   25
bears witness against the innocent."

There was a general shudder at this blasphemy.

William said meekly, " I leave our brethren to judge
whether this is the voice of Satan or not.   I can do
nothing but pray for you, Silas."   30

Poor Marner went out with that despair in his soul,
—that shaken trust in God and man, which is little
short of madness to a loving nature.   In the bitterness
of his wounded spirit, he said to himself, "*She* will cast

me off, too." And he reflected that, if she did not believe
the testimony against him, her whole faith must be upset
as his was. To people accustomed to reason about the
forms in which their religious feeling has incorporated
5 itself, it is difficult to enter into that simple, untaught
state of mind in which the form and the feeling have
never been severed by an act of reflection. We are apt
to think it inevitable that a man in Marner's position
should have begun to question the validity of an appeal
10 to the divine judgment by drawing lots ; but to him this
would have been an effort of independent thought such
as he had never known, and he must have made the
effort at a moment when all his energies were turned
into the anguish of disappointed faith. If there is an
15 angel who records the sorrows of men as well as their
sins, he knows how many and deep are the sorrows that
spring from false ideas for which no man is culpable.

Marner went home, and for a whole day sat alone,
stunned by despair, without any impulse to go to Sarah
20 and attempt to win her belief in his innocence. The
second day he took refuge from benumbing unbelief by
getting into his loom and working away as usual ; and
before many hours were past the minister and one of
the deacons came to him with the message from Sarah
25 that she held her engagement to him at an end. Silas
received the message mutely, and then turned away from
the messengers to work at his loom again. In little
more than a month from that time, Sarah was married
to William Dane ; and not long afterwards it was known
30 to the brethren in Lantern Yard that Silas Marner had
departed from the town.

CHAPTER II.

EVEN people whose lives have been made various by learning sometimes find it hard to keep a fast hold on their habitual views of life, on their faith in the Invisible, nay, on the sense that their past joys and sorrows are a real experience, when they are suddenly transported to a new land, where the beings around them know nothing of their history and share none of their ideas—where their mother earth shows another lap, and human life has other forms than those on which their souls have been nourished. Minds that have been unhinged from their old faith and love have perhaps sought this Lethean influence of exile, in which the past becomes dreamy because its symbols have all vanished, and the present, too, is dreamy because it is linked with no memories.   But even *their* experience may hardly enable them thoroughly to imagine what was the effect on a simple weaver like Silas Marner when he left his own country and people and came to settle in Raveloe.   Nothing could be more unlike his native town, set within sight of the widespread hillsides, than this low, wooded region, where he felt hidden even from the heavens by the screening trees and hedgerows.   There was nothing here, when he rose in the deep morning quiet and looked out on the dewy brambles and rank tufted grass, that seemed to have any relation with that life centering in Lantern Yard, which had once been to him the altar place of high dispensations.   The white-washed walls; the little pews where well-known figures entered with a subdued rustling, and where first one well-known voice and then another, pitched in a peculiar key

of petition, uttered phrases at once occult and familiar,
like the amulet worn on the heart ; the pulpit where the
minister delivered unquestioned doctrine, and swayed to
and fro, and handled the book in a long-accustomed
5 manner; the very pauses between the couplets of the
hymn, as it was given out, and the recurrent swell of
voices in song,—these things had been the channel of
divine influences to Marner; they were the fostering
home of his religious emotions; they were Christianity
10 and God's kingdom upon earth. A weaver who finds hard
words in his hymn book knows nothing of abstractions ;
as the little child knows nothing of parental love, but
only knows one face and one lap towards which it
stretches its arms for refuge and nurture.

15 And what could be more unlike that Lantern Yard
world than the world in Raveloe?—orchards looking
lazy with neglected plenty ; the large church in the wide
churchyard, which men gazed at, lounging at their own
doors, in service time ; the purple-faced farmers jogging
20 along the lanes or turning in at the Rainbow; homesteads, where men supped heavily and slept in the light
of the evening hearth, and where women seemed to be
laying up a stock of linen for the life to come. There
were no lips in Raveloe from which a word could fall
25 that would stir Silas Marner's benumbed faith to a sense
of pain. In the early ages of the world, we know, it was
believed that each territory was inhabited and ruled by
its own divinities, so that a man could cross the border-
ing heights and be out of the reach of his native gods,
30 whose presence was confined to the streams and the
groves and the hills among which he had lived from his
birth. And poor Silas was vaguely conscious of something not unlike the feeling of primitive men, when they
fled thus, in fear or in sullenness, from the face of an

unpropitious deity. It seemed to him that the Power
he had vainly trusted in among the streets and at the
prayer meetings was very far away from this land in
which he had taken refuge, where men lived in careless
abundance, knowing and needing nothing of that trust 5
which, for him, had been turned to bitterness. The
little light he possessed spread its beams so narrowly
that frustrated belief was a curtain broad enough to
create for him the blackness of night.

His first movement after the shock had been to work 10
in his loom; and he went on with this unremittingly,
never asking himself why, now he was come to Raveloe,
he worked far on into the night to finish the tale of
Mrs. Osgood's table linen sooner than she expected —
without contemplating beforehand the money she would 15
put into his hand for the work. He seemed to weave,
like the spider, from pure impulse, without reflection.
Every man's work, pursued steadily, tends in this way
to become an end in itself, and so to bridge over the
loveless chasms of his life. Silas's hand satisfied itself 20
with throwing the shuttle, and his eye with seeing the
little squares in the cloth complete themselves under
his effort. Then there were the calls of hunger; and
Silas, in his solitude, had to provide his own breakfast,
dinner, and supper, to fetch his own water from the 25
well, and put his own kettle on the fire; and all these
immediate promptings helped, along with the weaving,
to reduce his life to the unquestioning activity of a
spinning insect. He hated the thought of the past;
there was nothing that called out his love and fellowship 30
toward the strangers he had come amongst; and the
future was all dark, for there was no Unseen Love that
cared for him. Thought was arrested by utter bewilderment, now its old narrow pathway was closed, and

affection seemed to have died under the bruise that had fallen on its keenest nerves.

But at last Mrs. Osgood's table linen was finished, and Silas was paid in gold. His earnings in his native town, where he worked for a wholesale dealer, had been after a lower rate; he had been paid weekly, and of his weekly earnings a large proportion had gone to objects of piety and charity. Now, for the first time in his life, he had five bright guineas put into his hand; no man expected a share of them, and he loved no man that he should offer him a share. But what were the guineas to him who saw no vista beyond countless days of weaving? It was needless for him to ask that, for it was pleasant to him to feel them in his palm and look at their bright faces, which were all his own; it was another element of life, like the weaving and the satisfaction of hunger, subsisting quite aloof from the life of belief and love from which he had been cut off. The weaver's hand had known the touch of hard-won money even before the palm had grown to its full breadth; for twenty years mysterious money had stood to him as the symbol of earthly good and the immediate object of toil. He had seemed to love it little in the years when every penny had its purpose for him; for he loved the *purpose* then. But now, when all purpose was gone, that habit of looking towards the money and grasping it with a sense of fulfilled effort made a loam that was deep enough for the seeds of desire; and as Silas walked homeward across the fields in the twilight he drew out the money and thought it was brighter in the gathering gloom.

About this time an incident happened which seemed to open a possibility of some fellowship with his neighbors. One day, taking a pair of shoes to be mended, he saw the cobbler's wife seated by the fire, suffering from the terrible symptoms of heart disease and dropsy which he had witnessed as the precursors of his mother's death. He felt a rush of pity at the mingled sight and remembrance, and, recalling the relief his mother had 5 found from a simple preparation of foxglove, he promised Sally Oates to bring her something that would ease her, since the doctor did her no good. In this office of charity, Silas felt, for the first time since he had come to Raveloe, a sense of unity between his past and 10 present life, which might have been the beginning of his rescue from the insect-like existence into which his nature had shrunk. But Sally Oates's disease had raised her into a personage of much interest and importance among the neighbors, and the fact of her having found 15 relief from drinking Silas Marner's "stuff" became a matter of general discourse. When Doctor Kimble gave physic, it was natural that it should have an effect; but when a weaver, who came from nobody knew where, worked wonders with a bottle of brown waters, the occult 20 character of the process was evident. Such a sort of thing had not been known since the Wise Woman at Tarley died; and she had charms as well as "stuff"; everybody went to her when their children had fits. Silas Marner must be a person of the same sort, for 25 how did he know what would bring back Sally Oates's breath if he did n't know a fine sight more than that? The Wise Woman had words that she muttered to herself, so that you could n't hear what they were, and if she tied a bit of red thread round the child's toe the 30 while, it would keep off the water in the head. There were women in Raveloe, at that present time, who had worn one of the Wise Woman's little bags round their necks, and, in consequence, had never had an idiot

child, as Ann Coulter had. Silas Marner could very
likely do as much, and more; and now it was all clear
how he should have come from unknown parts and be
so "comical-looking." But Sally Oates must mind and
5 not tell the doctor, for he would be sure to set his face
against Marner; he was always angry about the Wise
Woman, and used to threaten those who went to her
that they should have none of his help any more.

Silas now found himself and his cottage suddenly
10 beset by mothers who wanted him to charm away the
whooping-cough or bring back the milk, and by men who
wanted stuff against the rheumatics or the knots in the
hands; and, to secure themselves against a refusal, the
applicants brought silver in their palms. Silas might
15 have driven a profitable trade in charms as well as in
his small list of drugs, but money on this condition was
no temptation to him: he had never known an impulse
towards falsity, and he drove one after another away
with growing irritation, for the news of him as a wise
20 man had spread even to Tarley, and it was long before
people ceased to take long walks for the sake of asking
his aid. But the hope in his wisdom was at length
changed into dread, for no one believed him when he
said he knew no charms and could work no cures, and
25 every man and woman who had an accident or a new
attack after applying to him set the misfortune down to
Master Marner's ill-will and irritated glances. Thus it
came to pass that his movement of pity towards Sally
Oates, which had given him a transient sense of brother-
30 hood, heightened the repulsion between him and his
neighbors, and made his isolation more complete.

Gradually the guineas, the crowns, and the half-crowns
grew to a heap, and Marner drew less and less for his
own wants, trying to solve the problem of keeping him-

self strong enough to work sixteen hours a day on as
small an outlay as possible. Have not men, shut up
in solitary imprisonment, found an interest in marking
the moments by straight strokes of a certain length on
the wall, until the growth of the sum of straight strokes, 5
arranged in triangles, has become a mastering purpose?
Do we not wile away moments of inanity or fatigued
waiting by repeating some trivial movement or sound,
until the repetition has bred a want, which is incipient
habit? That will help us to understand how the love of 10
accumulating money grows an absorbing passion in men
whose imaginations, even in the very beginning of their
hoard, showed them no purpose beyond it. Marner
wanted the heaps of ten to grow into a square, and then
into a larger square; and every added guinea, while it 15
was itself a satisfaction, bred a new desire. In this
strange world, made a hopeless riddle to him, he might,
if he had had a less intense nature, have sat weaving,
weaving, looking towards the end of his pattern or
towards the end of his web, till he forgot the riddle and 20
everything else but his immediate sensations; but the
money had come to mark off his weaving into periods,
and the money not only grew, but it remained with him.
He began to think it was conscious of him, as his loom
was, and he would on no account have exchanged those 25
coins, which had become his familiars, for other coins
with unknown faces. He handled them, he counted
them, till their form and color were like the satisfaction
of a thirst to him; but it was only in the night, when his
work was done, that he drew them out to enjoy their 30
companionship. He had taken up some bricks in his
floor underneath his loom, and here he had made a hole
in which he set the iron pot that contained his guineas
and silver coins, covering the bricks with sand whenever

he replaced them.   Not that the idea of being robbed
presented itself often or strongly to his mind.   Hoarding
was common in country districts in those days; there
were old laborers in the parish of Raveloe who were
5 known to have their savings by them, probably inside
their flock beds; but their rustic neighbors, though not
all of them as honest as their ancestors in the days of
King Alfred, had not imaginations bold enough to lay a
plan of burglary.   How could they have spent the money
10 in their own village without betraying themselves?   They
would be obliged to "run away,"—a course as dark and
dubious as a balloon journey.

So, year after year, Silas Marner had lived in this solitude, his guineas rising in the iron pot, and his life nar-
15 rowing and hardening itself more and more into a mere
pulsation of desire and satisfaction that had no relation
to any other being.   His life had reduced itself to the
functions of weaving and hoarding, without any con-
templation of an end towards which the functions tended.
20 The same sort of process has, perhaps, been undergone
by wiser men, when they have been cut off from faith
and love; only, instead of a loom and a heap of guineas,
they have had some erudite research, some ingenious
project, or some well-knit theory.   Strangely, Marner's
25 face and figure shrank and bent themselves into a constant mechanical relation to the objects of his life, so
that he produced the same sort of impression as a handle
or a crooked tube, which has no meaning standing apart.
The prominent eyes, that used to look trusting and
30 dreamy, now looked as if they had been made to see only
one kind of thing that was very small, like tiny grain, for
which they hunted everywhere; and he was so withered
and yellow that, though he was not yet forty, the children
always called him "Old Master Marner."

Yet even in this stage of withering a little incident happened which showed that the sap of affection was not all gone. It was one of his daily tasks to fetch his water from a well a couple of fields off, and for this purpose, ever since he came to Raveloe, he had had a brown earthenware pot, which he held as his most precious utensil among the very few conveniences he had granted himself. It had been his companion for twelve years, always standing on the same spot, always lending its handle to him in the early morning, so that its form had an expression for him of willing helpfulness, and the impress of its handle on his palm gave a satisfaction mingled with that of having the fresh, clear water. One day, as he was returning from the well, he stumbled against the step of the stile, and his brown pot, falling with force against the stones that overarched the ditch below him, was broken in three pieces. Silas picked up the pieces and carried them home with grief in his heart. The brown pot could never be of use to him any more, but he stuck the bits together and propped the ruin in its old place for a memorial.

This is the history of Silas Marner until the fifteenth year after he came to Raveloe. The livelong day he sat in his loom, his ear filled with its monotony, his eyes bent close down on the slow growth of sameness in the brownish web, his muscles moving with such even repetition that their pause seemed almost as much a constraint as the holding of his breath. But at night came his revelry; at night he closed his shutters and made fast his doors and drew forth his gold. Long ago the heap of coins had become too large for the iron pot to hold them, and he had made for them two thick leather bags, which wasted no room in their resting-place, but lent themselves flexibly to every corner. How the guineas shone as they came pouring out of the dark leather mouths! The silver bore no large proportion in amount to the gold, because the long pieces of linen which formed his chief work were always partly paid for in gold, and out of the silver he supplied his own bodily wants, choosing always the shillings and sixpences to spend in this way. He loved the guineas best, but he would not change the silver, — the crowns and half-crowns that were his own earnings, begotten by his labor; he loved them all. He spread them out in heaps and bathed his hands in them; then he counted them and set them up in regular piles, and felt their rounded outline between his thumb and fingers, and thought fondly of the guineas that were only half earned by the work in his loom, as if they had been unborn children — thought of the guineas that were coming slowly through the coming years, through all his life, which spread far away before him, the end quite hidden by countless days of weaving. No wonder his thoughts were still with his loom and his money when he made his journeys through the fields and the lanes to fetch and carry home his work, so that his steps never wandered to the hedge banks and the laneside in search of the once familiar herbs; these, too, belonged to the past, from which his life had shrunk away, like a rivulet that has sunk far down from the grassy fringe of its old breadth into a little shivering thread that cuts a groove for itself in the barren sand.

But about the Christmas of that fifteenth year a second great change came over Marner's life, and his history became blent in a singular manner with the life of his neighbors.

CHAPTER III.

THE greatest man in Raveloe was Squire Cass, who lived in the large red house with the handsome flight of stone steps in front and the high stables behind it, nearly opposite the church. He was only one among several landed parishioners, but he alone was honored with the title of Squire ; for though Mr. Osgood's family was also understood to be of timeless origin — the Raveloe imagination having never ventured back to that fearful blank when there were no Osgoods — still, he merely owned the farm he occupied ; whereas Squire Cass had a tenant or two, who complained of the game to him quite as if he had been a lord.

It was still that glorious war time which was felt to be a peculiar favor of Providence towards the landed interest, and the fall of prices had not yet come to carry the race of small squires and yeomen down that road to ruin for which extravagant habits and bad husbandry were plentifully anointing their wheels. I am speaking now in relation to Raveloe and the parishes that resembled it ; for our old-fashioned country life had many different aspects, as all life must have when it is spread over a various surface and breathed on variously by multitudinous currents, from the winds of heaven to the thoughts of men, which are forever moving and crossing each other with incalculable results. Raveloe lay low among the bushy trees and the rutted lanes, aloof from the currents of industrial energy and Puritan earnestness ; the rich ate and drank freely, accepting gout and apoplexy as things that ran mysteriously in respectable families, and the poor thought that the rich were entirely in the right of it

to lead a jolly life; besides, their feasting caused a mul-
tiplication of orts, which were the heirlooms of the poor.
Betty Jay scented the boiling of Squire Cass's hams, but
her longing was arrested by the unctuous liquor in which
5 they were boiled; and when the seasons brought round
the great merry-makings, they were regarded on all hands
as a fine thing for the poor. For the Raveloe feasts
were like the rounds of beef and the barrels of ale, — they
were on a large scale and lasted a good while, especially
10 in the winter time. After ladies had packed up their
best gowns and topknots in bandboxes, and had incurred
the risk of fording streams on pillions with the precious
burden in rainy or snowy weather, when there was no
knowing how high the water would rise, it was not to be
15 supposed that they looked forward to a brief pleasure.
On this ground it was always contrived in the dark seasons, when there was little work to be done and the hours
were long, that several neighbors should keep open house
in succession. So soon as Squire Cass's standing dishes
20 diminished in plenty and freshness his guests had nothing to do but to walk a little higher up the village to Mr.
Osgood's, at the Orchards, and they found hams and
chines uncut, pork pies with the scent of the fire in them,
spun butter in all its freshness, — everything, in fact, that
25 appetites at leisure could desire, in perhaps greater perfection, though not in greater abundance, than at Squire
Cass's.

For the Squire's wife had died long ago, and the Red
House was without that presence of the wife and mother
30 which is the fountain of wholesome love and fear in
parlor and kitchen; and this helped to account not only
for there being more profusion than finished excellence
in the holiday provisions, but also for the frequency with
which the proud Squire condescended to preside in the

parlor of the Rainbow rather than under the shadow of
his own dark wainscot; perhaps, also, for the fact that
his sons had turned out rather ill. Raveloe was not a
place where moral censure was severe, but it was thought
a weakness in the Squire that he had kept all his sons at 5
home in idleness; and, though some license was to be
allowed to young men whose fathers could afford it,
people shook their heads at the courses of the second
son, Dunstan, commonly called Dunsey Cass, whose taste
for swapping and betting might turn out to be a sowing 10
of something worse than wild oats. To be sure, the
neighbors said, it was no matter what became of Dunsey,
— a spiteful, jeering fellow, who seemed to enjoy his
drink the more when other people went dry, — always
provided that his doings did not bring trouble on a family 15
like Squire Cass's, with a monument in the church and
tankards older than King George. But it would be a
thousand pities if Mr. Godfrey, the eldest, a fine, open-
faced, good-natured young man, who was to come into
the land some day, should take to going along the same 20
road with his brother, as he had seemed to do of late.
If he went on in that way, he would lose Miss Nancy
Lammeter; for it was well known that she had looked
very shyly on him ever since last Whitsuntide twelvemonth, when there was so much talk about his being 25
away from home days and days together. There was
something wrong, more than common — that was quite
clear; for Mr. Godfrey did n't look half so fresh-colored
and open as he used to do. At one time everybody was
saying, What a handsome couple he and Miss Nancy 30
Lammeter would make! and if she could come to be
mistress at the Red House, there would be a fine change,
for the Lammeters had been brought up in that way that
they never suffered a pinch of salt to be wasted, and yet

everybody in their household had of the best, according to his place. Such a daughter-in-law would be a saving to the old Squire, if she never brought a penny to her fortune; for it was to be feared that, notwithstanding his
5 incomings, there were more holes in his pocket than the one where he put his own hand in. But if Mr. Godfrey didn't turn over a new leaf, he might say "good-by" to Miss Nancy Lammeter.

It was the once hopeful Godfrey who was standing,
10 with his hands in his side pockets and his back to the fire, in the dark wainscoted parlor one late November afternoon in that fifteenth year of Silas Marner's life at Raveloe. The fading gray light fell dimly on the walls decorated with guns, whips, and foxes' brushes, on coats
15 and hats flung on the chairs, on tankards sending forth a scent of flat ale, and on a half-choked fire, with pipes propped up in the chimney corners, — signs of a domestic life destitute of any hallowing charm, with which the look of gloomy vexation on Godfrey's blonde face was in sad
20 accordance. He seemed to be waiting and listening for some one's approach, and presently the sound of a heavy step, with an accompanying whistle, was heard across the large empty entrance hall.

The door opened, and a thick-set, heavy-looking young
25 man entered, with the flushed face and the gratuitously elated bearing which mark the first stage of intoxication. It was Dunsey, and at the sight of him Godfrey's face parted with some of its gloom to take on the more active expression of hatred. The handsome brown spaniel that lay on
30 the hearth retreated under the chair in the chimney corner.

"Well, Master Godfrey, what do you want with me?" said Dunsey in a mocking tone. "You're my elders and betters, you know; I was obliged to come when you sent for me."

"Why, this is what I want — and just shake yourself sober and listen, will you?" said Godfrey savagely. He had himself been drinking more than was good for him, trying to turn his gloom into uncalculating anger. "I want to tell you I must hand over that rent of Fowler's to the Squire, or else tell him I gave it you; for he's threatening to distrain for it, and it'll all be out soon, whether I tell him or not. He said, just now, before he went out, he should send word to Cox to distrain if Fowler didn't come and pay up his arrears this week. The Squire's short o' cash and in no humor to stand any nonsense; and you know what he threatened if ever he found you making away with his money again. So, see and get the money, and pretty quickly, will you?"

"Oh!" said Dunsey sneeringly, coming nearer to his brother and looking in his face. "Suppose, now, you get the money yourself, and save me the trouble, eh? Since you was so kind as to hand it over to me, you'll not refuse me the kindness to pay it back for me; it was your brotherly love made you do it, you know."

Godfrey bit his lips and clenched his fist. "Don't come near me with that look, else I'll knock you down."

"Oh, no, you won't," said Dunsey, turning away on his heel, however. "Because I'm such a good-natured brother, you know. I might get you turned out of house and home and cut off with a shilling any day. I might tell the Squire how his handsome son was married to that nice young woman, Molly Farren, and was very unhappy because he couldn't live with his drunken wife, and I should slip into your place as comfortable as could be. But you see I don't do it — I'm so easy and good-natured. You'll take any trouble for me. You'll get the hundred pounds for me; I know you will."

"How can I get the money?" said Godfrey, quivering.

"I have n't a shilling to bless myself with. And it's a lie that you'd slip into my place; you'd get yourself turned out, too, that's all. For if you begin telling tales, I'll follow. Bob's my father's favorite; you know that
5 very well. He'd only think himself well rid of you."

"Never mind," said Dunsey, nodding his head sideways as he looked out of the window. "It 'ud be very pleasant to me to go in your company; you're such a handsome brother, and we've always been so fond of
10 quarreling with one another, I should n't know what to do without you. But you'd like better for us both to stay at home together; I know you would. So you'll manage to get that little sum o' money, and I'll bid you good-by, though I'm sorry to part."

15 Dunstan was moving off, but Godfrey rushed after him and seized him by the arm, saying, with an oath:

"I tell you, I have no money; I can get no money."

"Borrow of old Kimble."

"I tell you, he won't lend me any more, and I shan't
20 ask him."

"Well, then, sell Wildfire."

"Yes, that's easy talking. I must have the money directly."

"Well, you've only got to ride him to the hunt to-
25 morrow. There'll be Bryce and Keating there, for sure. You'll get more bids than one."

"I daresay, and get back home at eight o'clock, splashed up to the chin. I'm going to Mrs. Osgood's birthday dance."

30 "Oho!" said Dunsey, turning his head on one side and trying to speak in a small, mincing treble. "And there's sweet Miss Nancy coming; and we shall dance with her and promise never to be naughty again and be taken into favor and—"

" Hold your tongue about Miss Nancy, you fool,"
said Godfrey, turning red, " else I 'll throttle you."

" What for ? " said Dunsey, still in an artificial tone,
but taking a whip from the table and beating the butt end
of it on his palm. " You 've a very good chance. I 'd
advise you to creep up her sleeve again ; it 'ud be saving
time, if Molly should happen to take a drop too much
laudanum some day and make a widower of you. Miss
Nancy would n't mind being a second, if she did n't know
it. And you 've got a good-natured brother, who 'll keep
your secret well, because you 'll be so very obliging to
him."

" I 'll tell you what it is," said Godfrey, quivering and
pale again, " my patience is pretty near at an end. If
you 'd a little more sharpness in you, you might know
that you may urge a man a bit too far and make one leap
as easy as another. I don't know but what it is so now.
I may as well tell the Squire everything myself ; I should
get you off my back, if I got nothing else. And, after
all, he 'll know some time. She 's been threatening to
come herself and tell him. So, don't flatter yourself that
your secrecy 's worth any price you choose to ask. You
drain me of money till I have got nothing to pacify *her*
with, and she 'll do as she threatens some day. It 's all
one. I 'll tell my father everything myself, and you may
go to the devil."

Dunsey perceived that he had overshot his mark, and
that there was a point at which even the hesitating Godfrey might be driven into decision. But he said, with
an air of unconcern :

" As you please ; but I 'll have a draught of ale first."
And, ringing the bell, he threw himself across two
chairs, and began to rap the window seat with the handle
of his whip.

Godfrey stood, still with his back to the fire, uneasily
moving his fingers among the contents of his side pockets
and looking at the floor. That big, muscular frame of
his held plenty of animal courage, but helped him to no
5 decision when the dangers to be braved were such as
could neither be knocked down nor throttled. His
natural irresolution and moral cowardice were exagger-
ated by a position in which dreaded consequences
seemed to press equally on all sides, and his irritation
10 had no sooner provoked him to defy Dunstan and anticipate all possible betrayals than the miseries he must
bring on himself by such a step seemed more unendurable
to him than the present evil. The results of confession
were not contingent — they were certain — whereas be-
15 trayal was not certain. From the near vision of that
certainty he fell back on suspense and vacillation with
a sense of repose. The disinherited son of a small
squire, equally disinclined to dig and to beg, was almost
as helpless as an uprooted tree, which, by the favor of
20 earth and sky, has grown to a handsome bulk on the
spot where it first shot upward. Perhaps it would have
been possible to think of digging with some cheerfulness
if Nancy Lammeter were to be won on those terms; but,
since he must irrevocably lose *her* as well as the inherit-
25 ance, and must break every tie but the one that degraded
him and left him without motive for trying to recover
his better self, he could imagine no future for himself on
the other side of confession but that of " 'listing for a
soldier," — the most desperate step, short of suicide, in
30 the eyes of respectable families. No! he would rather
trust to casualties than to his own resolve, — rather go
on sitting at the feast and sipping the wine he loved,
though with the sword hanging over him and terror in
his heart, than rush away into the cold darkness where

there was no pleasure left. The utmost concession to Dunstan about the horse began to seem easy, compared with the fulfillment of his own threat. But his pride would not let him recommence the conversation otherwise than by continuing the quarrel. Dunstan was waiting for this, and took his ale in shorter draughts than usual.

"It's just like you," Godfrey burst out in a bitter tone, "to talk about my selling Wildfire in that cool way,— the last thing I've got to call my own and the best bit of horse flesh I ever had in my life. And if you'd got a spark of pride in you, you'd be ashamed to see the stables emptied and everybody sneering about it. But it's my belief you'd sell yourself, if it was only for the pleasure of making somebody feel he'd got a bad bargain."

"Ay, ay," said Dunstan, very placably, "you do me justice, I see. You know I'm a jewel for 'ticing people into bargains. For which reason I advise you to let *me* sell Wildfire. I'd ride him to the hunt to-morrow for you with pleasure. I shouldn't look so handsome as you in the saddle, but it's the horse they'll bid for, and not the rider."

"Yes, I daresay — trust my horse to you!"

"As you please," said Dunstan, rapping the window seat again with an air of great unconcern. "It's *you* have got to pay Fowler's money; it's none of my business. You received the money from him when you went to Bramcote, and *you* told the Squire it wasn't paid. I'd nothing to do with that; you chose to be so obliging as to give it me, — that was all. If you don't want to pay the money, let it alone; it's all one to me. But I was willing to accommodate you by undertaking to sell the horse, seeing it's not convenient to you to go so far to-morrow."

Godfrey was silent for some moments. He would have liked to spring on Dunstan, wrench the whip from his hand, and flog him to within an inch of his life, and no bodily fear could have deterred him; but he was mastered by another sort of fear, which was fed by feelings stronger even than his resentment. When he spoke again it was in a half-conciliatory tone.

"Well, you mean no nonsense about the horse, eh? You'll sell him all fair and hand over the money? If you don't, you know, everything 'ull go to smash, for I've got nothing else to trust to. And you'll have less pleasure in pulling the house over my head when your own skull's to be broken, too."

"Ay, ay," said Dunstan, rising; "all right. I thought you'd come round. I'm the fellow to bring old Bryce up to the scratch. I'll get you a hundred and twenty for him, if I get you a penny."

"But it'll perhaps rain cats and dogs to-morrow, as it did yesterday, and then you can't go," said Godfrey, hardly knowing whether he wished for that obstacle or not.

"Not *it*," said Dunstan. "I'm always lucky in my weather. It might rain if you wanted to go yourself. You never hold trumps, you know — I always do. You've got the beauty, you see, and I've got the luck, so you must keep me by you for your crooked sixpence; you'll *ne*-ver get along without me."

"Confound you, hold your tongue!" said Godfrey impetuously. "And take care to keep sober to-morrow, else you'll get pitched on your head coming home, and Wildfire might be the worse for it."

"Make your tender heart easy," said Dunstan, opening the door. "You never knew me see double when I'd got a bargain to make; it 'ud spoil the fun. Besides, whenever I fall, I'm warranted to fall on my legs."

With that Dunstan slammed the door behind him, and left Godfrey to that bitter rumination on his personal circumstances which was now unbroken from day to day save by the excitement of sporting, drinking, card playing, or the rarer and less oblivious pleasure of seeing 5 Miss Nancy Lammeter. The subtle and varied pains springing from the higher sensibility that accompanies higher culture are perhaps less pitiable than that dreary absence of impersonal enjoyment and consolation which leaves ruder minds to the perpetual urgent companion- 10 ship of their own griefs and discontents. The lives of those rural forefathers, whom we are apt to think very prosaic figures — men whose only work was to ride round their land, getting heavier and heavier in their saddles, and who passed the rest of their days in the half-listless 15 gratification of senses dulled by monotony — had a certain pathos in them, nevertheless. Calamities came to *them,* too, and their early errors carried hard consequences; perhaps the love of some sweet maiden, the image of purity, order, and calm, had opened their eyes to the 20 vision of a life in which the days would not seem too long, even without rioting; but the maiden was lost, and the vision passed away, and then what was left to them, especially when they had become too heavy for the hunt or for carrying a gun over the furrows, but to drink and 25 get merry, or to drink and get angry, so that they might be independent of variety, and say over again with eager emphasis the things they had said already any time that twelvemonth? Assuredly, among these flushed and dull-eyed men there were some whom — thanks to their native 30 human kindness — even riot could never drive into brutality; men who, when their cheeks were fresh, had felt the keen point of sorrow or remorse, had been pierced by the reeds they leaned on, or had lightly put

their limbs in fetters from which no struggle could loose
them; and under these sad circumstances, common to
us all, their thoughts could find no resting-place outside
the ever trodden round of their own petty history.

5   That, at least, was the condition of Godfrey Cass
in this six-and-twentieth year of his life. A movement
of compunction, helped by those small indefinable influ-
ences· which every personal relation exerts on a pliant
nature, had urged him into a secret marriage, which was
10 a blight on his life. It was an ugly story of low passion,
delusion, and waking from delusion, which needs not
to be dragged from the privacy of Godfrey's bitter
memory. He had long known that the delusion was
partly due to a trap laid for him by Dunstan, who saw
15 in his brother's degrading marriage the means of grati-
fying at once his jealous hate and his cupidity. And
if Godfrey could have felt himself simply a victim, the
iron bit that destiny had put into his mouth would have
chafed him less intolerably. If the curses he muttered
20 half aloud when he was alone had had no other object
than Dunstan's diabolical cunning, he might have shrunk
less from the consequences of avowal. But he had
something else to curse, — his own vicious folly, which
now seemed as mad and unaccountable to him as almost
25 all our follies and vices do when their promptings have
long passed away. For four years he had thought of
Nancy Lammeter, and wooed her with tacit, patient worship, as the woman who made him think of the future
with joy; she would be his wife, and would make home
30 lovely to him, as his father's home had never been, and
it would be easy, when she was always near, to shake off
those foolish habits that were no pleasures, but only
a feverish way of annulling vacancy. Godfrey's was an
essentially domestic nature, bred up in a home where the

"Conscience doth make cowards of us all." Shakespeare

hearth had no smiles, and where the daily habits were
not chastised by the presence of household order. His
easy disposition made him fall in unresistingly with the
family courses, but the need of some tender permanent
affection, the longing for some influence that would make 5
the good he preferred easy to pursue, caused the neatness,
purity, and liberal orderliness of the Lammeter household, sunned by the smile of Nancy, to seem like
those fresh, bright hours of the morning when tempta-
tions go to sleep and leave the ear open to the voice of 10
the good angel, inviting to industry, sobriety, and peace.
And yet the hope of this paradise had not been enough
to save him from a course which shut him out of it
forever. Instead of keeping fast hold of the strong silken
rope by which Nancy would have drawn him safe to the 15
green banks where it was easy to step firmly, he had let
himself be dragged back into mud and slime, in which
it was useless to struggle. He had made ties for himself
which robbed him of all wholesome motive and were a
constant exasperation. 20

Still, there was one position worse than the present : it
was the position he would be in when the ugly secret
was disclosed ; and the desire that continually triumphed
over every other was that of warding off the evil day
when he would have to bear the consequences of his 25
father's violent resentment for the wound inflicted on
his family pride — would have, perhaps, to turn his back
on that hereditary ease and dignity which, after all, was
a sort of reason for living, and would carry with him the
certainty that he was banished forever from the sight 30
and esteem of Nancy Lammeter. The longer the interval, the more chance there was of deliverance from some,
at least, of the hateful consequences to which he had
sold himself ; the more opportunities remained for him

to snatch the strange gratification of seeing Nancy and
gathering some faint indications of her lingering regard.
Towards this gratification he was impelled fitfully every
now and then, after having passed weeks in which he
5 had avoided her as the far-off, bright-winged prize that
only made him spring forward and find his chain all the
more galling.) One of those fits of yearning was on him
now, and it would have been strong enough to have
persuaded him to trust Wildfire to Dunstan rather than
10 disappoint the yearning, even if he had not had another
reason for his disinclination towards the morrow's hunt.
That other reason was the fact that the morning's meet
was near Batherley, the market town where the unhappy
woman lived whose image became more odious to him
15 every day; and to his thought the whole vicinage was
haunted by her. The yoke a man creates for himself by
wrongdoing will breed hate in the kindliest nature; and
the good-humored, affectionate-hearted Godfrey Cass was
fast becoming a bitter man, visited by cruel wishes, that
20 seemed to enter and depart and enter again, like demons
who had found in him a ready-garnished home.

What was he to do this evening to pass the time? He
might as well go to the Rainbow and hear the talk about
the cock-fighting; everybody was there, and what else
25 was there to be done? Though, for his own part he did
not care a button for cock-fighting. Snuff, the brown
spaniel, who had placed herself in front of him, and had
been watching him for some time, now jumped up in
impatience for the expected caress. But Godfrey thrust
30 her away without looking at her, and left the room,
followed humbly by the unresenting Snuff — perhaps
because she saw no other career open to her.

CHAPTER IV.

DUNSTAN CASS, setting off in the raw morning, at the judiciously quiet pace of a man who is obliged to ride to cover on his hunter, had to take his way along the lane which, at its farther extremity, passed by the piece of uninclosed ground called the Stone-pit, where stood 5 the cottage, once a stone-cutter's shed, now for fifteen years inhabited by Silas Marner. The spot looked very dreary at this season, with the moist trodden clay about it and the red muddy water high up in the deserted quarry. That was Dunstan's first thought as he ap- 10 proached it; the second was that the old fool of a weaver, whose loom he heard rattling already, had a great deal of money hidden somewhere. How was it that he, Dunstan Cass, who had often heard talk of Marner's miserliness, had never thought of suggesting to Godfrey that he 15 should frighten or persuade the old fellow into lending the money on the excellent security of the young Squire's prospects? The resource occurred to him now as so easy and agreeable, especially as Marner's hoard was likely to be large enough to leave Godfrey a handsome 20 surplus beyond his immediate needs and enable him to accommodate his faithful brother, that he had almost turned the horse's head towards home again. Godfrey would be ready enough to accept the suggestion; he would snatch eagerly at a plan that might save him from 25 parting with Wildfire. But when Dunstan's meditation reached this point the inclination to go on grew strong and prevailed. He didn't want to give Godfrey that pleasure; he preferred that Master Godfrey should be vexed. Moreover, Dunstan enjoyed the self-important 30

consciousness of having a horse to sell and the opportunity of driving a bargain, swaggering, and possibly
taking somebody in. He might have all the satisfaction
attendant on selling his brother's horse, and not the less
5 have the further satisfaction of setting Godfrey to borrow
Marner's money. So he rode on to cover.

Bryce and Keating were there, as Dunstan was quite
sure they would be — he was such a lucky fellow.

"Heyday!" said Bryce, who had long had his eye
10 on Wildfire, "you're on your brother's horse to-day;
how's that?"

"Oh, I've swapped with him," said Dunstan, whose
delight in lying, grandly independent of utility, was not
to be diminished by the likelihood that his hearer would
15 not believe him; "Wildfire's mine now."

"What! has he swapped with you for that big-boned
hack of yours?" said Bryce, quite aware that he should
get another lie in answer.

"Oh, there was a little account between us," said
20 Dunsey carelessly, "and Wildfire made it even. I accommodated him by taking the horse, though it was
against my will, for I'd got an itch for a mare o' Jortin's,
— as rare a bit o' blood as ever you threw your leg
across. But I shall keep Wildfire, now I've got him,
25 though I'd a bid of a hundred and fifty for him the other
day from a man over at Flitton — he's buying for Lord
Cromleck — a fellow with a cast in his eye and a green
waistcoat. But I mean to stick to Wildfire; I sha'n't get
a better at a fence in a hurry. The mare's got more
30 blood, but she's a bit too weak in the hindquarters."

Bryce of course divined that Dunstan wanted to sell
the horse, and Dunstan knew that he divined it (horse
dealing is only one of many human transactions carried
on in this ingenious manner); and they both considered

that the bargain was in its first stage, when Bryce replied
ironically:

"I wonder at that now. I wonder you mean to keep
him; for I never heard of a man who didn't want to sell
his horse getting a bid of half as much again as the   5
horse was worth. You'll be lucky if you get a hundred."

Keating rode up now, and the transaction become
more complicated. It ended in the purchase of the
horse by Bryce for a hundred and twenty, to be paid on
the delivery of Wildfire, safe and sound, at the Batherley   10
stables. It did occur to Dunsey that it might be wise
for him to give up the day's hunting, proceed at once
to Batherley, and, having waited for Bryce's return, hire
a horse to carry him home with the money in his pocket.
But the inclination for a run, encouraged by confidence   15
in his luck and by a draught of brandy from his pocket
pistol at the conclusion of the bargain, was not easy to
overcome, especially with a horse under him that would
take the fences to the admiration of the field. Dunstan,
however, took one fence too many, and got his horse   20
pierced with a hedge stake. His own ill-favored person,
which was quite unmarketable, escaped without injury;
but poor Wildfire, unconscious of his price, turned on
his flank and painfully panted his last. It happened that
Dunstan, a short time before, having had to get down to   25
arrange his stirrup, had muttered a good many curses at
this interruption, which had thrown him in the rear of
the hunt near the moment of glory, and under this
exasperation had taken the fences more blindly. He
would soon have been up with the hounds again, when   30
the fatal accident happened; and hence he was between
eager riders in advance, not troubling themselves about
what happened behind them, and far-off stragglers, who
were as likely as not to pass quite aloof from the line of

road in which Wildfire had fallen. Dunstan, whose
nature it was to care more for immediate annoyances
than for remote consequences, no sooner recovered his
legs and saw that it was all over with Wildfire than
5 he felt a satisfaction at the absence of witnesses to a
position which no swaggering could make enviable.
Reënforcing himself, after his shake, with a little brandy
and much swearing, he walked as fast as he could to
a coppice on his right hand, through which it occurred
10 to him that he could make his way to Batherley without
danger of encountering any member of the hunt. His
first intention was to hire a horse there and ride home
forthwith, for to walk many miles without a gun in his
hand and along an ordinary road was as much out of the
15 question to him as to other spirited young men of his
kind. He did not much mind about taking the bad
news to Godfrey, for he had to offer him at the same
time the resource of Marner's money; and if Godfrey
kicked, as he always did, at the notion of making a fresh
20 debt from which he himself got the smallest share of
advantage, why, he wouldn't kick long. Dunstan felt
sure he could worry Godfrey into anything. The idea of
Marner's money kept growing in vividness now the want
of it had become immediate. The prospect of having to
25 make his appearance with the muddy boots of a pedes-
trian at Batherley, and to encounter the grinning queries
of stablemen, stood unpleasantly in the way of his
impatience to be back at Raveloe and carry out his
felicitous plan; and a casual visitation of his waistcoat
30 pocket, as he was ruminating, awakened his memory to
the fact that the two or three small coins his forefinger
encountered there were of too pale a color to cover that
small debt without payment of which the stable keeper
had declared he would never do any more business with

Dunsey Cass. After all, according to the direction in
which the run had brought him, he was not so very much
farther from home than he was from Batherley; but
Dunsey, not being remarkable for clearness of head, was
only led to this conclusion by the gradual perception 5
that there were other reasons for choosing the unprec-
edented course of walking home. It was now nearly
four o'clock, and a mist was gathering; the sooner he
got into the road the better. He remembered having
crossed the road and seen the finger post only a little 10
while before Wildfire broke down; so, buttoning his
coat, twisting the lash of his hunting whip compactly
round the handle, and rapping the tops of his boots with
a self-possessed air, as if to assure himself that he was
not at all taken by surprise, he set off with the sense that 15
he was undertaking a remarkable feat of bodily exertion,
which somehow and at some time he should be able to
dress up and magnify to the admiration of a select circle
at the Rainbow. When a young gentleman like Dunsey
is reduced to so exceptional a mode of locomotion as 20
walking, a whip in his hand is a desirable corrective to a
too bewildering, dreamy sense of unwontedness in his
position; and Dunstan, as he went along through the
gathering mist, was always rapping his whip somewhere.
It was Godfrey's whip, which he had chosen to take 25
without leave, because it had a gold handle; of course
no one could see, when Dunstan held it, that the name
Godfrey Cass was cut in deep letters on that gold handle
—they could only see that it was a very handsome whip.
Dunsey was not without fear that he might meet some 30
acquaintance in whose eyes he would cut a pitiable figure,
for mist is no screen when people get close to each
other; but when he at last found himself in the well-
known Raveloe lanes without having met a soul he

silently remarked that that was part of his usual good
luck. But now the mist, helped by the evening darkness,
was more of a screen than he desired, for it hid the ruts
into which his feet were liable to slip — hid everything,
5 so that he had to guide his steps by dragging his whip
along the low bushes in advance of the hedgerow. He
must soon, he thought, be getting near the opening at
the Stone-pits; he should find it out by the break in the
hedgerow. He found it out, however, by another circum-
10 stance which he had not expected, — namely, by certain
gleams of light, which he presently guessed to proceed
from Silas Marner's cottage. That cottage and the
money hidden within it had been in his mind continually
during his walk, and he had been imagining ways of
15 cajoling and tempting the weaver to part with the
immediate possession of his money for the sake of
receiving interest. Dunstan felt as if there must be a
little frightening added to the cajolery, for his own
arithmetical convictions were not clear enough to afford
20 him any forcible demonstration as to the advantages of
interest; and as for security, he regarded it vaguely as a
means of cheating a man by making him believe that he
would be paid. Altogether, the operation on the miser's
mind was a task that Godfrey would be sure to hand over
25 to his more daring and cunning brother — Dunstan had
made up his mind to that; and by the time he saw the
light gleaming through the chinks of Marner's shutters
the idea of a dialogue with the weaver had become so
familiar to him that it occurred to him as quite a natural
30 thing to make the acquaintance forthwith. There might
be several conveniences attending this course; the weaver
had possibly got a lantern, and Dunstan was tired of
feeling his way. He was still nearly three-quarters of a
mile from home, and the lane was becoming unpleasantly

slippery, for the mist was passing into rain. He turned
up the bank, not without some fear lest he might miss
the right way, since he was not certain whether the light
were in front or on the side of the cottage. But he felt
the ground before him cautiously with his whip handle, 5
and at last arrived safely at the door. He knocked
loudly, rather enjoying the idea that the old fellow would
be frightened at the sudden noise. He heard no movement in reply; all was silence in the cottage. Was the
weaver gone to bed, then? If so, why had he left a 10
light? That was a strange forgetfulness in a miser.
Dunstan knocked still more loudly, and, without pausing
for a reply, pushed his fingers through the latch hole,
intending to shake the door and pull the latchstring up
and down, not doubting that the door was fastened. But, 15
to his surprise, at this double motion the door opened,
and he found himself in front of a bright fire which lit
up every corner of the cottage, — the bed, the loom, the
three chairs, and the table, and showed him that Marner
was not there. 20

Nothing at that moment could be much more inviting
to Dunsey than the bright fire on the brick hearth; he
walked in and seated himself by it at once. There was
something in front of the fire, too, that would have been
inviting to a hungry man if it had been in a different 25
stage of cooking. It was a small bit of pork suspended
from the kettle hanger by a string passed through a large
door key, in a way known to primitive housekeepers
unpossessed of jacks. But the pork had been hung
at the farthest extremity of the hanger, apparently to 30
prevent the roasting from proceeding too rapidly during
the owner's absence. The old staring simpleton had hot
meat for his supper, then, thought Dunstan. People had
always said he lived on moldy bread, on purpose to

check his appetite.   But where could he be at this time
and on such an evening, leaving his supper in this stage
of preparation and his door unfastened?   Dunstan's own
recent difficulty in making his way suggested to him that
5 the weaver had perhaps gone outside his cottage to fetch
in fuel, or for some such brief purpose, and had slipped
into the Stone-pit.   That was an interesting idea to
Dunstan, carrying consequences of entire novelty.   If
the weaver was dead, who had a right to his money?
10 Who would know where his money was hidden?   *Who
would know that anybody had come to take it away?*   He
went no farther into the subtleties of evidence; the pressing question, Where *is* the money? now took such entire
possession of him as to make him quite forget that the
15 weaver's death was not a certainty.   A dull mind, once
arriving at an inference that flatters a desire, is rarely
able to retain the impression that the notion from which
the inference started was purely problematic.   And Dunstan's mind was as dull as the mind of a possible felon
20 usually is.   There were only three hiding-places where
he had ever heard of cottagers' hoards being found, —
the thatch, the bed, and a hole in the floor.   Marner's
cottage had no thatch; and Dunstan's first act, after a
train of thought made rapid by the stimulus of cupidity,
25 was to go up to the bed; but while he did so his eyes
traveled eagerly over the floor, where the bricks, distinct
in the firelight, were discernible under the sprinkling of
sand.   But not everywhere; for there was one spot, and
one only, which was quite covered with sand, and sand
30 showing the marks of fingers, which had apparently been
careful to spread it over a given space.   It was near the
treadles of the loom.   In an instant Dunstan darted to
that spot, swept away the sand with his whip, and,
inserting the thin end of the hook between the bricks,

found that they were loose. In haste he lifted up two
bricks, and saw what he had no doubt was the object of
his search; for what could there be but money in those
two leathern bags? And, from their weight, they must
be filled with guineas. Dunstan felt round the hole to 5
be certain that it held no more; then hastily replaced the
bricks and spread the sand over them. Hardly more
than five minutes had passed since he entered the cottage,
but it seemed to Dunstan like a long while; and, though
he was without any distinct recognition of the possibility 10
that Marner might be alive and might reënter the cottage
at any moment, he felt an undefinable dread laying hold
on him as he rose to his feet with the bags in his hand.
He would hasten out into the darkness, and then consider
what he should do with the bags. He closed the door 15
behind him immediately, that he might shut in the stream
of light; a few steps would be enough to carry him
beyond betrayal by the gleams from the shutter chinks
and the latch hole. The rain and darkness had got
thicker, and he was glad of it; though it was awkward 20
walking with both hands filled, so that it was as much as
he could do to grasp his whip along with one of the bags.
But when he had gone a yard or two he might take his
time. So he stepped forward into the darkness.

CHAPTER V.

WHEN Dunstan Cass turned his back on the cottage, Silas Marner was not more than a hundred yards away from it, plodding along from the village, with a sack thrown round his shoulders as an overcoat, and with a horn lantern is his hand. His legs were weary, but his mind was at ease, free from the presentiment of change. The sense of security more frequently springs from habit than from conviction, and for this reason it often subsists after such a change in the conditions as might have been expected to suggest alarm. The lapse of time during which a given event has not happened is, in this logic of habit, constantly alleged as a reason why the event should never happen, even when the lapse of time is precisely the added condition which makes the event imminent. A man will tell you that he has worked in a mine for forty years unhurt by an accident as a reason why he should apprehend no danger, though the roof is beginning to sink; and it is often observable that the older a man gets the more difficult it is to him to retain a believing conception of his own death. This influence of habit was necessarily strong in a man whose life was so monotonous as Marner's, who saw no new people and heard of no new events to keep alive in him the idea of the unexpected and the changeful; and it explains simply enough why his mind could be at ease, though he had left his house and his treasure more defenseless than usual. Silas was thinking with double complacency of his supper; first, because it would be hot and savory, and, secondly, because it would cost him nothing. For the little bit of pork was a present from that excellent housewife, Miss Priscilla Lammeter, to whom he had this day carried home a handsome piece of linen; and it was only on occasion of a present like this that Silas indulged himself with roast meat. Supper was his favorite meal, because 5 it came at his time of revelry, when his heart warmed over his gold; whenever he had roast meat he always chose to have it for supper. But this evening he had no sooner ingeniously knotted his string fast round his bit of pork, twisted the string according to rule over his door 10 key, passed it through the handle, and made it fast on the hanger than he remembered that a piece of very fine twine was indispensable to his " setting up " a new piece of work in his loom early in the morning. It had slipped his memory, because, in coming from Mr. Lammeter's, 15 he had not had to pass through the village; but to lose time by going on errands in the morning was out of the question. It was a nasty fog to turn out into, but there were things Silas loved better than his own comfort; so, drawing his pork to the extremity of the hanger 20 and arming himself with his lantern and his old sack, he set out on what, in ordinary weather, would have been a twenty minutes' errand. He could not have locked his door without undoing his well-knotted string and retarding his supper; it was not worth his while to make that 25 sacrifice. What thief would find his way to the Stone-pits on such a night as this? and why should he come on this particular night, when he had never come through all the fifteen years before? These questions were not distinctly present in Silas's mind; they merely serve to 30 represent the vaguely felt foundation of his freedom from anxiety.

He reached his door in much satisfaction that his errand was done; he opened it, and to his short-sighted

eyes everything remained as he had left it, except that
the fire sent out a welcome increase of heat. He trod
about the floor while putting by his lantern and throwing
aside his hat and sack, so as to merge the marks of
5 Dunstan's feet on the sand in the marks of his own
nailed boots. Then he moved his pork nearer to the
fire and sat down to the agreeable business of tending
the meat and warming himself at the same time.

Any one who had looked at him as the red light shone
10 upon his pale face, strange, straining eyes, and meager
form would perhaps have understood the mixture of contemptuous pity, dread, and suspicion with which he was
regarded by his neighbors in Raveloe. Yet few men
could be more harmless than poor Marner. In his truth-
15 ful, simple soul not even the growing greed and worship
of gold could beget any vice directly injurious to others.
The light of his faith quite put out and his affections
made desolate, he had clung with all the force of his
nature to his work and his money; and, like all objects
20 to which a man devotes himself, they had fashioned him
into correspondence with themselves. His loom, as he
wrought in it without ceasing, had in its turn wrought
on him, and confirmed more and more the monotonous
craving for its monotonous response. His gold, as he
25 hung over it and saw it grow, gathered his power of
loving together into a hard isolation like its own.

As soon as he was warm he began to think it would
be a long while to wait till after supper before he drew
out his guineas, and it would be pleasant to see them on
30 the table before him as he ate his unwonted feast. For
joy is the best of wine, and Silas's guineas were a golden
wine of that sort.

He rose and placed his candle unsuspectingly on the
floor near his loom, swept away the sand without noticing

any change, and removed the bricks. The sight of the
empty hole made his heart leap violently, but the belief
that his gold was gone could not come at once — only
terror, and the eager effort to put an end to the terror.
He passed his trembling hand all about the hole, trying 5
to think it possible that his eyes had deceived him; then
he held the candle in the hole and examined it curiously,
trembling more and more. At last he shook so violently
that he let fall the candle, and lifted his hands to his
head, trying to steady himself, that he might think. Had 10
he put his gold somewhere else, by a sudden resolution
last night, and then forgotten it? A man falling into
dark waters seeks a momentary footing, even on sliding
stones; and Silas, by acting as if he believed in false
hopes, warded off the moment of despair. He searched 15
in every corner; he turned his bed over and shook it
and kneaded it; he looked in his brick oven where he
laid his sticks. When there was no other place to
be searched he kneeled down again and felt once more
all round the hole. There was no untried refuge left for 20
a moment's shelter from the terrible truth.

Yes, there was a sort of refuge which always comes
with the prostration of thought under an overpowering
passion : it was that expectation of impossibilities, that
belief in contradictory images, which is still distinct from 25
madness, because it is capable of being dissipated by
the external fact. Silas got up from his knees, trembling,
and looked round at the table; didn't the gold lie there,
after all? The table was bare. Then he turned and
looked behind him, — looked all round his dwelling, 30
seeming to strain his brown eyes after some possible
appearance of the bags where he had already sought
them in vain. He could see every object in his cottage
— and his gold was not there.

Again he put his trembling hands to his head, and gave a wild, ringing scream, the cry of desolation. For a few moments after he stood motionless; but the cry had relieved him from the first maddening pressure of 5 the truth. He turned and tottered towards his loom, and got into the seat where he worked, instinctively seeking this as the strongest assurance of reality.

And now that all the false hopes had vanished, and the first shock of certainty was past, the idea of a thief 10 began to present itself, and he entertained it eagerly, because a thief might be caught and made to restore the gold. The thought brought some new strength with it, and he started from his loom to the door. As he opened it the rain beat in upon him, for it was falling more and 15 more heavily. There were no footsteps to be tracked on such a night — footsteps? When had the thief come? During Silas's absence in the daytime the door had been locked, and there had been no marks of any inroad on his return by daylight. And in the evening, too, he said 20 to himself, everything was the same as when he had left it. The sand and bricks looked as if they had not been moved. *Was* it a thief who had taken the bags? or was it a cruel power that no hands could reach which had delighted in making him a second time desolate? He 25 shrank from this vaguer dread, and fixed his mind with struggling effort on the robber with hands, who could be reached by hands. His thoughts glanced at all the neighbors who had made any remarks or asked any questions which he might now regard as a ground of 30 suspicion. There was Jem Rodney, a known poacher, and otherwise disreputable; he had often met Marner in his journeys across the fields, and had said something jestingly about the weaver's money. Nay, he had once irritated Marner by lingering at the fire when he called to light his pipe, instead of going about his business. Jem Rodney was the man — there was ease in the thought. Jem could be found and made to restore the money. Marner did not want to punish him, but only to get back his gold which had gone from him and left his soul like a forlorn traveler on an unknown desert. The robber must be laid hold of. Marner's ideas of legal authority were confused, but he felt that he must go and proclaim his loss; and the great people in the village, — the clergyman, the constable, and Squire Cass, — would make Jem Rodney, or somebody else, deliver up the stolen money. He rushed out in the rain, under the stimulus of this hope, forgetting to cover his head, not caring to fasten his door; for he felt as if he had nothing left to lose. He ran swiftly, till want of breath compelled him to slacken his pace as he was entering the village at the turning close to the Rainbow.

The Rainbow, in Marner's view, was a place of luxurious resort for rich and stout husbands, whose wives had superfluous stores of linen; it was the place where he was likely to find the powers and dignities of Raveloe, and where he could most speedily make his loss public. He lifted the latch and turned into the bright bar or kitchen on the right hand, where the less lofty customers of the house were in the habit of assembling, the parlor on the left being reserved for the more select society in which Squire Cass frequently enjoyed the double pleasure of conviviality and condescension. But the parlor was dark to-night, the chief personages who ornamented its circle being all at Mrs. Osgood's birthday dance, as Godfrey Cass was. And, in consequence of this, the party on the high-screened seats in the kitchen was more numerous than usual; several personages, who would otherwise have been admitted into the parlor and enlarged

the opportunity of hectoring and condescension for their betters, being content this evening to vary their enjoyment by taking their spirits and water where they could themselves hector and condescend in company that
5 called for beer.

CHAPTER VI.

THE conversation, which was at a high pitch of animation when Silas approached the door of the Rainbow,
had, as usual, been slow and intermittent when the
company first assembled. The pipes began to be puffed
in a silence which had an air of severity, the more 5
important customers, who drank spirits and sat nearest
the fire, staring at each other as if a bet were depending
on the first man who winked; while the beer drinkers,
chiefly men in fustian jackets and smock frocks, kept their
eyelids down and rubbed their hands across their mouths, 10
as if their draughts of beer were a funeral duty attended
with embarrassing sadness. At last, Mr. Snell, the landlord, a man of a neutral disposition, accustomed to stand
aloof from human differences as those of beings who
were all alike in need of liquor, broke silence by saying 15
in a doubtful tone to his cousin, the butcher:

"Some folks 'ud say that was a fine beast you druv
in yesterday, Bob?"

The butcher, a jolly, smiling, red-haired man, was
not disposed to answer rashly. He gave a few puffs 20
before he spat and replied, "And they wouldn't be fur
wrong, John."

After this feeble, delusive thaw, the silence set in as
severely as before.

"Was it a red Durham?" said the farrier, taking up 25
the thread of discourse after the lapse of a few minutes.

The farrier looked at the landlord, and the landlord
looked at the butcher, as the person who must take the
responsibility of answering.

"Red it was," said the butcher, in his good-humored, husky treble, "and a Durham it was."

"Then you need n't tell *me* who you bought it of," said the farrier, looking round with some triumph; "I know who it is has got the red Durhams o' this countryside. And she'd a white star on her brow, I 'll bet a penny?" The farrier leaned forward with his hands on his knees as he put this question, and his eyes twinkled knowingly.

"Well, yes — she might," said the butcher slowly, considering that he was giving a decided affirmative. "I don't say contrairy."

"I knew that very well," said the farrier, throwing himself backward again and speaking defiantly; "if *I* don't know Mr. Lammeter's cows, I should like to know who does — that's all. And as for the cow you've bought, bargain or no bargain, I 've been at the drenching of her — contradick me who will."

The farrier looked fierce, and the mild butcher's conversational spirit was roused a little.

"I'm not for contradicking no man," he said; "I'm for peace and quietness. Some are for cutting long ribs — I'm for cutting 'em short myself; but *I* don't quarrel with 'em. All I say is, it's a lovely carkiss; and anybody as was reasonable, it 'ud bring tears into their eyes to look at it."

"Well, it's the cow as I drenched, whatever it is," pursued the farrier angrily; "and it was Mr. Lammeter's cow, else you told a lie when you said it was a red Durham."

"I tell no lies," said the butcher, with the same mild huskiness as before, "and I contradick none — not if a man was to swear himself black; he 's no meat o' mine, nor none o' my bargains. All I say is, it's a lovely carkiss. And what I say I 'll stick to; but I 'll quarrel wi' no man."

"No," said the farrier, with bitter sarcasm, looking
at the company generally, "and p'rhaps you arn't pig-
headed, and p'rhaps you didn't say the cow was a red
Durham, and p'rhaps you didn't say she 'd got a star on
her brow — stick to that, now you 're at it."   5

"Come, come," said the landlord; "let the cow alone.
The truth lies atween you; you 're both right and both
wrong, as I allays say. And as for the cow's being Mr.
Lammeter's, I say nothing to that; but this I say, as the
Rainbow's the Rainbow. And for the matter o' that, if 10
the talk is to be o' the Lammeters, _you_ know the most
upo' that head, eh, Mr. Macey? You remember when
first Mr. Lammeter's father come into these parts and
took the Warrens?"

Mr. Macey, tailor and parish clerk, the latter of which 15
functions rheumatism had of late obliged him to share
with a small-featured young man who sat opposite him,
held his white head on one side and twirled his thumbs
with an air of complacency, slightly seasoned with
criticism. He smiled pityingly, in answer to the land- 20
lord's appeal, and said:

"Ay, ay, I know, I know; but I let other folks talk.
I've laid by now, and gev up to the young uns. Ask
them as have been to school at Tarley; they've learnt
pernouncing — that 's come up since my day."   25

"If you 're pointing at me, Mr. Macey," said the
deputy clerk, with an air of anxious propriety, "I 'm
nowise a man to speak out of my place. As the psalm
says:

> 'I know what 's right, nor only so,   30
> But also practice what I know.'"

"Well, then, I wish you 'd keep hold o' the tune, when
it 's set for you; if you 're for prac_tic_ing, I wish you 'd
prac_tice_ that," said a large, jocose-looking man, an excel-

lent wheelwright in his weekday capacity, but on Sundays
leader of the choir. He winked, as he spoke, at two of
the company, who were known officially as the "bassoon"
and the "key-bugle," in the confidence that he was ex-
5 pressing the sense of the musical profession in Raveloe.

Mr. Tookey, the deputy clerk, who shared the unpopu-
larity common to deputies, turned very red, but replied,
with careful moderation, "Mr. Winthrop, if you'll bring
me any proof as I'm in the wrong, I'm not the man to
10 say I won't alter. But there's people set up their own
ears for a standard, and expect the whole choir to follow
'em. There may be two opinions, I hope."

"Ay, ay," said Mr. Macey, who felt very well satisfied
with this attack on youthful presumption; "you're right
15 there, Tookey. There's allays two 'pinions; there's the
'pinion a man has of himsen, and there's the 'pinion
other folks have on him. There'd be two 'pinions about
a cracked bell, if the bell could hear itself."

"Well, Mr. Macey," said poor Tookey, serious amidst
20 the general laughter, "I undertook to partially fill up the
office of parish clerk, by Mr. Crackenthorp's desire, whenever your infirmities should make you unfitting; and it's
one of the rights thereof to sing in the choir — else why
have you done the same yourself?"

25 "Ah! but the old gentleman and you are two folks,"
said Ben Winthrop. "The old gentleman's got a gift.
Why, the Squire used to invite him to take a glass only
to hear him sing the 'Red Rovier'; didn't he, Mr. Macey?
It's a nat'ral gift. There's my little lad Aaron, — he's
30 got a gift; he can sing a tune off straight, like a throstle.
But as for you, Master Tookey, you'd better stick to your
'amens'; your voice is well enough when you keep it up
in your nose. It's your inside as isn't right made for
music; it's no better nor a hollow stalk."

This kind of unflinching frankness was the most piquant form of joke to the company at the Rainbow, and Ben Winthrop's insult was felt by everybody to have capped Mr. Macey's epigram.

"I see what it is plain enough," said Mr. Tookey, unable to keep cool any longer. "There's a conspiracy to turn me out o' the choir, as I shouldn't share the Christmas money — that's where it is. But I shall speak to Mr. Crackenthorp; I'll not be put upon by no man."

"Nay, nay, Tookey," said Ben Winthrop. "We'll pay you your share to keep out of it — that's what we'll do. There's things folks 'ud pay to be rid on besides varmin."

"Come, come," said the landlord, who felt that paying people for their absence was a principle dangerous to society; "a joke's a joke. We're all good friends here, I hope. We must give and take. You're both right and you're both wrong, as I say. I agree wi' Mr. Macey here, as there's two opinions; and if mine was asked, I should say they're both right. Tookey's right and Winthrop's right, and they've only got to split the difference and make themselves even."

The farrier was puffing his pipe rather fiercely, in some contempt at this trivial discussion. He had no ear for music himself, and never went to church, as being of the medical profession, and likely to be in requisition for delicate cows. But the butcher, having music in his soul, had listened with a divided desire for Tookey's defeat and for the preservation of the peace.

"To be sure," he said, following up the landlord's conciliatory view, "we're fond of our old clerk; it's nat'ral, and him used to be such a singer, and got a brother as is known for the first fiddler in this countryside. Eh, it's a pity but what Solomon lived in our village, and

could give us a tune when we liked; eh, Mr. Macey? I'd
keep him in liver and lights for nothing—that I would."

"Ay, ay," said Mr. Macey, in the height of complacency; "our family's been known for musicianers as far
5 back as anybody can tell. But them things are dying
out, as I tell Solomon every time he comes round; there's
no voices like what there used to be, and there's nobody
remembers what we remember, if it isn't the old crows."

"Ay, you remember when first Mr. Lammeter's father
10 come into these parts, don't you, Mr. Macey?" said the
landlord.

"I should think I did," said the old man, who had now
gone through that complimentary process necessary to
bring him up to the point of narration; "and a fine old
15 gentleman he was—as fine and finer nor the Mr. Lammeter as now is. He came from a bit north'ard, so far
as I could ever make out. But there's nobody rightly
knows about those parts; only it couldn't be far north'ard,
nor much different from this country, for he brought a
20 fine breed o' sheep with him, so there must be pastures
there, and everything reasonable. We heared tell as
he'd sold his own land to come and take the Warrens,
and that seemed odd for a man as had land of his own,
to come and rent a farm in a strange place. But they
25 said it was along of his wife's dying—though there's
reasons in things as nobody knows on—that's pretty
much what I've made out; yet some folks are so wise,
they'll find you fifty reasons straight off, and all the while
the real reason's winking at 'em in the corner, and they
30 niver see't. Howsomever, it was soon seen as we'd got
a new parish'ner as know'd the rights and customs o'
things and kep a good house and was well looked on by
everybody. And the young man—that's the Mr. Lammeter as now is, for he'd niver a sister—soon begun to

court Miss Osgood— that's the sister o' the Mr. Osgood
as now is, and a fine handsome lass she was — eh, you
can't think; they pretend this young lass is like her,
but that's the way wi' people as don't know what come
before 'em. *I* should know, for I helped the old rector,   5
Mr. Drumlow as was; I helped him marry 'em."

Here Mr. Macey paused; he always gave his narrative
in instalments, expecting to be questioned according to
precedent.

"Ay, and a partic'lar thing happened, did n't it, Mr.   10
Macey, so as you were likely to remember that marriage?"
said the landlord, in a congratulatory tone.

"I should think there did — a *very* partic'lar thing,"
said Mr. Macey, nodding sideways. "For Mr. Drumlow
— poor old gentleman, I was fond on him, though he'd   15
got a bit confused in his head, what wi' age and wi' taking a drop o' summat warm when the service come of a
cold morning. And young Mr. Lammeter he'd have no
way but he must be married in Janiwary, which, to be
sure, 's a unreasonable time to be married in, for it is n't   20
like a christening or a burying, as you can't help; and so
Mr. Drumlow — poor old gentleman, I was fond on him —
but when he come to put the questions, he put 'em by
the rule o' contrairy, like, and he says, 'Wilt thou have
this man to thy wedded wife?' says he, and then he says,   25
'Wilt thou have this woman to thy wedded husband?'
says he. But the partic'larest thing of all is as nobody
took any notice on it but me, and they answered straight
off 'yes,' like as if it had been me saying 'Amen' i' the
right place, without listening to what went before."   30

"But *you* knew what was going on well enough, did n't
you, Mr. Macey? You were live enough, eh?" said the
butcher.

"Lor bless you!" said Mr. Macey, pausing and smil-

ing in pity at the impotence of his hearer's imagination,
" why, I was all of a tremble. It was as if I 'd been a
coat pulled by the two tails, like ; for I could n't stop
the parson — I could n't take upon me to do that — and
5 yet I said to myself, I says, ' Suppose they should n't be
fast married, 'cause the words are contrairy ? ' and my
head went working like a mill, for I was allays uncommon
for turning things over and seeing all round 'em ; and I
says to myself, ' Is 't the meanin' or the words as makes
10 folks fast i' wedlock ? ' For the parson meant right, and
the bride and bridegroom meant right. But, then, when
I come to think on it, meanin' goes but a little way i'
most things, for you may mean to stick things together
and your glue may be bad, and then where are you ?
15 And so I says to mysen, ' It is n't the meanin'; it 's the
glue. And I was worreted as if I 'd got three bells to
pull at once, when we went into the vestry, and they begun to sign their names. But where 's the use o' talking ?
— you can't think what goes on in a 'cute man's inside."

20 " But you held in for all that, did n't you, Mr. Macey ? "
said the landlord.

"Ay, I held in tight till I was by mysen wi' Mr. Drumlow, and then I out wi' everything, but respectful, as I
allays did. And he made light on it, and he says, ' Pooh,
25 pooh, Macey, make yourself easy,' he says; ' it 's neither
the meaning nor the words — it 's the re*ges*ter does it —
that 's the glue.' So you see he settled it easy; for
parsons and doctors know everything by heart, like, so as
they are n't worreted wi' thinking what 's the rights and
30 wrongs o' things, as I 'n been many and many 's the time.
And, sure enough, the wedding turned out all right, on'y
poor Mrs. Lammeter — that 's Miss Osgood as was — died
afore the lasses was growed up; but for prosperity and
everything respectable, there 's no family more looked on."

Every one of Mr. Macey's audience had heard this story many times, but it was listened to as if it had been a favorite tune, and at certain points the puffing of the pipes was momentarily suspended that the listeners might give their whole minds to the expected words. But there was more to come ; and Mr. Snell, the landlord, duly put the leading question.

"Why, old Mr. Lammeter had a pretty fortin, did n't they say, when he come into these parts?"

"Well, yes," said Mr. Macey ; "but I daresay it's as much as this Mr. Lammeter's done to keep it whole. For there was allays a talk as nobody could get rich on the Warrens ; though he holds it cheap, for it's what they call Charity Land."

"Ay, and there's few folks know so well as you how it come to be Charity Land, eh, Mr. Macey?" said the butcher.

"How should they?" said the old clerk, with some contempt. "Why, my grandfather made the groom's livery for that Mr. Cliff as came and built the big stables at the Warrens. Why, they 're stables four times as big as Squire Cass's, for he thought o' nothing but hosses and hunting, Cliff did n't, — a Lunnon tailor, some folks said, as had gone mad wi' cheating. For he could n't ride ; lor bless you ! they said he 'd got no more grip o' the hoss than if his legs had been cross-sticks. My grandfather heared old Squire Cass say so many and many a time. But ride he would as if Old Harry had been a-driving him ; and he 'd a son, a lad o' sixteen, and nothing would his father have him do, but he must ride and ride — though the lad was frighted, they said. And it was a common saying as the father wanted to ride the tailor out o' the lad and make a gentlemen on him — not but what I 'm a tailor myself, but in respect as God

made me such, I'm proud on it, for 'Macey, tailor,' 's
been wrote up over our door since afore the Queen's
heads went out on the shillings. But Cliff, he was
ashamed o' being called a tailor, and he was sore vexed
5 as his riding was laughed at, and nobody o' the gentlefolks hereabout could abide him. Howsomever, the
poor lad got sickly and died, and the father did n't live
long after him, for he got queerer nor ever, and they said
he used to go out i' the dead o' the night, wi' a lantern in
10 his hand, to the stables, and set a lot o' lights burning,
for he got as he could n't sleep, and there he'd stand,
cracking his whip and looking at his hosses ; and they
said it was a mercy as the stables did n't get burnt down
wi' the poor dumb creaturs in 'em. But at last he died
15 raving, and they found as he'd left all his property,
Warrens and all, to a Lunnon Charity, and that's how
the Warrens come to be Charity Land ; though, as for
the stables, Mr. Lammeter never uses 'em — they're out
o' all charicter — lor bless you ! if you was to set the
20 doors a-banging in 'em, it 'ud sound like thunder half o'er
the parish."

"Ay, but there's more going on in the stables than what
folks see by daylight, eh, Mr. Macey ? " said the landlord.

" Ay, ay ; go that way of a dark night, that's all," said
25 Mr. Macey, winking mysteriously, "and then make believe, if you like, as you did n't see lights i' the stables,
nor hear the stamping o' the hosses, nor the cracking o'
the whips, and howling, too, if it's tow'rt daybreak.
'Cliff's Holiday' has been the name of it ever sin' I were
30 a boy ; that's to say, some said as it was the holiday Old
Harry gev him from roasting, like. That's what my
father told me, and he was a reasonable man, though
there's folks nowadays know what happened afore they
were born better nor they know their own business."

"What do you say to that, eh, Dowlas?" said the landlord, turning to the farrier, who was swelling with impatience for his cue. "There's a nut for *you* to crack."

Mr. Dowlas was the negative spirit in the company,
and was proud of his position.

"Say? I say what a man *should* say as does n't shut
his eyes to look at a finger post. I say, as I'm ready to
wager any man ten pound, if he'll stand out wi' me any
dry night in the pasture before the Warren stables, as
we shall neither see lights nor hear noises, if it is n't the
blowing of our own noses. That's what I say, and I've
said it many a time; but there's nobody 'ull ventur a
ten-pun' note on their ghos'es as they make so sure
of."

"Why, Dowlas, that's easy betting, that is," said Ben
Winthrop. "You might as well bet a man as he would n't
catch the rheumatise if he stood up to 's neck in the pool
of a frosty night. It 'ud be fine fun for a man to win his
bet as he'd catch the rheumatise. Folks as believe in
Cliff's Holiday are n't a-going to ventur near it for a
matter o' ten pound."

"If Master Dowlas wants to know the truth on it," said
Mr. Macey, with a sarcastic smile, tapping his thumbs together, "he's no call to lay any bet — let him go and stan'
by himself — there's nobody 'ull hinder him; and then he
can let the parish'ners know if they're wrong."

"Thank you! I'm obliged to you," said the farrier,
with a snort of scorn. "If folks are fools, it's no business
o' mine. *I* don't want to make out the truth about
ghos'es; I know it a'ready. But I'm not against a bet —
everything fair and open. Let any man bet me ten pound
as I shall see Cliff's Holiday, and I'll go and stand by
myself. I want no company. I'd as lief do it as I'd fill
this pipe."

"Ah, but who's to watch you, Dowlas, and see you do it? That's no fair bet," said the butcher.

"No fair bet?" replied Mr. Dowlas angrily. "I should like to hear any man stand up and say I want to bet unfair.
5 Come now, Master Lundy, I should like to hear you say it."

"Very like you would," said the butcher. "But it's no business o' mine. You're none o' my bargains, and I aren't a-going to try and 'bate your price. If anybody'll bid for you at your own vallying, let him. I'm for peace
10 and quietness, I am."

"Yes, that's what every yapping cur is when you hold a stick up at him," said the farrier. "But I'm afraid o' neither man nor ghost, and I'm ready to lay a fair bet. *I* aren't a turn-tail cur."

15 "Ay, but there's this in it, Dowlas," said the landlord, speaking in a tone of much candor and tolerance. "There's folks, i' my opinion, they can't see ghos'es, not if they stood as plain as a pikestaff before 'em. And there's reason i' that. For there's my wife, now, can't
20 smell, nor if she'd the strongest o' cheese under her nose. I never see'd a ghost myself; but then I says to myself, 'Very like I haven't got the smell for 'em.' I mean, putting a ghost for a smell, or else contrairiways. And so I'm for holding with both sides; for, as I say, the truth
25 lies between 'em. And if Dowlas was to go and stand, and say he'd never seen a wink o' Cliff's Holiday all the night through, I'd back him; and if anybody said as Cliff's Holiday was certain sure for all that, I'd back *him* too. For the smell's what I go by."

30 The landlord's analogical argument was not well received by the farrier,— a man intensely opposed to compromise.

"Tut, tut," he said, setting down his glass with refreshed irritation, "what's the smell got to do with it?

Did ever a ghost give a man a black eye ?   That's what I should like to know.   If ghos'es want me to believe in 'em, let 'em leave off skulking i' the dark and i' lone places ; let 'em come where there's company and candles."   5

"As if ghos'es 'ud want to be believed in by anybody so ignirant !" said Mr. Macey, in deep disgust at the farrier's crass incompetence to apprehend the conditions of ghostly phenomena.

CHAPTER VII.

YET the next moment there seemed to be some evidence
that ghosts had a more condescending disposition than
Mr. Macey attributed to them ; for the pale, thin figure of
Silas Marner was suddenly seen standing in the warm light,
5 uttering no word, but looking round at the company with
his strange, unearthly eyes. The long pipes gave a simul-
taneous movement, like the antennæ of startled insects,
and every man present, not excepting even the skeptical
farrier, had an impression that he saw, not Silas Marner
10 in the flesh, but an apparition ; for the door by which
Silas had entered was hidden by the high-screened seats,
and no one had noticed his approach. Mr. Macey, sitting
a long way off the ghost, might be supposed to have felt
an argumentative triumph, which would tend to neutralize
15 his share of the general alarm. Had he not always said
that when Silas Marner was in that strange trance of his
his soul went loose from his body ? Here was the demonstration ; nevertheless, on the whole, he would have been
as well contented without it. For a few moments there
20 was a dead silence, Marner's want of breath and agitation not allowing him to speak. The landlord, under the
habitual sense that he was bound to keep his house open
to all company, and confident in the protection of his
unbroken neutrality, at last took on himself the task of
25 adjuring the ghost.

"Master Marner," he said, in a conciliatory tone,
"what's lacking to you ? What's your business here ?"

"Robbed !" said Silas gaspingly. "I've been robbed !
I want the constable — and the Justice — and Squire Cass
30 — and Mr. Crackenthorp."

"Lay hold on him, Jem Rodney," said the landlord, the idea of a ghost subsiding; "he's off his head, I doubt. He's wet through."

Jem Rodney was the outermost man, and sat conveniently near Marner's standing-place; but he declined to give his services.

"Come and lay hold on him yourself, Mr. Snell, if you've a mind," said Jem, rather sullenly. "He's been robbed, and murdered, too, for what I know," he added, in a muttering tone.

"Jem Rodney!" said Silas, turning and fixing his strange eyes on the suspected man.

"Ay, Master Marner, what do you want wi' me?" said Jem, trembling a little, and seizing his drinking can as a defensive weapon.

"If it was you stole my money," said Silas, clasping his hands entreatingly and raising his voice to a cry, "give it me back—and I won't meddle with you. I won't set the constable on you. Give it me back, and I'll let you—I'll let you have a guinea."

"Me stole your money!" said Jem angrily. "I'll pitch this can at your eye if you talk o' *my* stealing your money."

"Come, come, Master Marner," said the landlord, now rising resolutely and seizing Marner by the shoulder, "if you've got any information to lay, speak it out sensible, and show as you're in your right mind, if you expect anybody to listen to you. You're as wet as a drownded rat. Sit down and dry yourself, and speak straight forrard."

"Ah, to be sure, man," said the farrier, who began to feel that he had not been quite on a par with himself and the occasion. "Let's have no more staring and screaming, else we'll have you strapped for a madman. That

was why I did n't speak at the first — thinks I, the man 's
run mad."

"Ay, ay, make him sit down," said several voices at
once, well pleased that the reality of ghosts remained still
5 an open question.

The landlord forced Marner to take off his coat, and
then to sit down on a chair aloof from every one else, in
the center of the circle and in the direct rays of the fire.
The weaver, too feeble to have any distinct purpose be-
10 yond that of getting help to recover his money, submitted
unresistingly. The transient fears of the company were
now forgotten in their strong curiosity, and all faces were
turned towards Silas, when the landlord, having seated
himself again, said:

15 "Now then, Master Marner, what 's this you 've got to
say — as you 've been robbed ?   Speak out."

"He 'd better not say again as it was me robbed him,"
cried Jem Rodney hastily. "What could I ha' done with
his money ?   I could as easy steal the parson's surplice
20 and wear it."

"Hold your tongue, Jem, and let 's hear what he 's got
to say," said the landlord. "Now then, Master Marner."

Silas now told his story, under frequent questioning as
the mysterious character of the robbery became evident.
25 This strangely novel situation of opening his trouble to
his Raveloe neighbors, of sitting in the warmth of a
hearth not his own, and feeling the presence of faces and
voices which were his nearest promise of help had doubtless its influence on Marner, in spite of his passionate pre-
30 occupation with his loss. Our consciousness rarely regis-
ters the beginning of a growth within us any more than
without us ; there have been many circulations of the sap
before we detect the smallest sign of the bud.

The slight suspicion with which his hearers at first lis-

tened to him gradually melted away before the convincing
simplicity of his distress ; it was impossible for the neighbors to doubt that Marner was telling the truth, not because they were capable of arguing at once from the nature
of his statements to the absence of any motive for making 5
them falsely, but because, as Mr. Macey observed, "folks
as had the devil to back 'em were not likely to be so
mushed " as poor Silas was. Rather, from the strange
fact that the robber had left no traces, and had happened
to know the nick of time, utterly incalculable by mortal 10
agents, when Silas would go away from home without lock-
ing his door, the more probable conclusion seemed to be
that his disreputable intimacy in that quarter, if it ever
existed, had been broken up, and that, in consequence,
this ill turn had been done to Marner by somebody it was 15
quite in vain to set the constable after. Why this preter-
natural felon should be obliged to wait till the door was
left unlocked was a question which did not present itself.

"It is n't Jem Rodney as has done this work, Master
Marner," said the landlord. "You mus' n't be a-casting 20
your eye at poor Jem. There may be a bit of a reckoning
against Jem for the matter of a hare or so if anybody was
bound to keep their eyes staring open and niver to wink ;
but Jem 's been a-sitting here drinking his can, like the de-
centest man i' the parish, since before you left your house, 25
Master Marner, by your own account."

"Ay, ay," said Mr. Macey ; "let 's have no accusing o'
the innicent. That is n't the law. There must be folks
to swear again' a man before he can be ta'en up. Let 's
have no accusing o' the innicent, Master Marner." 30

Memory was not so utterly torpid in Silas that it could
not be awakened by these words. With a movement of
compunction as new and strange to him as everything else
within the last hour, he started from his chair and went

close up to Jem, looking at him as if he wanted to assure himself of the expression in his face.

"I was wrong," he said; "yes, yes — I ought to have thought. There's nothing to witness against you, Jem. Only you'd been into my house oftener than anybody else, and so you came into my head. I don't accuse you — I won't accuse anybody — only," he added, lifting up his hands to his head and turning away with bewildered misery, "I try — I try to think where my guineas can be."

"Ay, ay, they're gone where it's hot enough to melt 'em, I doubt," said Mr. Macey.

"Tchuh!" said the farrier. And then he asked, with a cross-examining air, "How much money might there be in the bags, Master Marner?"

"Two hundred and seventy-two pounds, twelve and six-pence, last night when I counted it," said Silas, seating himself again, with a groan.

"Pooh! why, they'd be none so heavy to carry. Some tramp's been in, that's all; and as for the no footmarks and the bricks and the sand being all right — why, your eyes are pretty much like a insect's, Master Marner; they're obliged to look so close, you can't see much at a time. It's my opinion as if I'd been you or you'd been me — for it comes to the same thing — you would n't have thought you'd found everything as you left it. But what I vote is as two of the sensiblest o' the company should go with you to Master Kench, the constable's — he's ill i' bed, I know that much — and get him to appoint one of us his deppity; for that's the law, and I don't think anybody 'ull take upon him to contradick me there. It is n't much of a walk to Kench's; and then, if it's me as is deppity, I'll go back with you, Master Marner, and examine your premises; and if anybody's got any fault to find with that, I'll thank him to stand up and say it out like a man."

By this pregnant speech the farrier had reëstablished
his self-complacency, and waited with confidence to hear
himself named as one of the superlatively sensible
men.

"Let us see how the night is, though," said the land- 5
lord, who also considered himself personally concerned in
this proposition. "Why, it rains heavy still," he said, returning from the door.

"Well, I 'm not the man to be afraid o' the rain," said
the farrier. "For it 'll look bad when Justice Malam 10
hears as respectable men like us had a information laid
before 'em and took no steps."

The landlord agreed with this view, and after taking the
sense of the company, and duly rehearsing a small ceremony known in high ecclesiastical life as the *nolo episco-* 15
pari, he consented to take on himself the chill dignity of
going to Kench's. But, to the farrier's strong disgust, Mr.
Macey now started an objection to his proposing himself
as a deputy constable; for that oracular old gentleman,
claiming to know the law, stated, as a fact delivered to 20
him by his father, that no doctor could be a constable.

"And you 're a doctor, I reckon, though you 're only a
cow-doctor, for a fly 's a fly, though it may be a hossfly,"
concluded Mr. Macey, wondering a little at his own
"'cuteness." 25

There was a hot debate upon this, the farrier being of
course indisposed to renounce the quality of doctor, but
contending that a doctor could be a constable if he liked —
the law meant he need n't be one if he did n't like. Mr.
Macey thought this was nonsense, since the law was not 30
likely to be fónder of doctors than of other folks. Moreover, if it was in the nature of doctors more than of other
men not to like being constables, how came Mr. Dowlas to
be so eager to act in that capacity?

"*I* don't want to act the constable," said the farrier, driven into a corner by this merciless reasoning ; "and there's no man can say it of me, if he'd tell the truth. But if there's to be any jealousy and envying about going to
5 Kench's in the rain, let them go as like it — you won't get me to go, I can tell you."

By the landlord's intervention, however, the dispute was accommodated. Mr. Dowlas consented to go as a second person disinclined to act officially ; and so poor
10 Silas, furnished with some old coverings, turned out with his two companions into the rain again, thinking of the long night hours before him, not as those do who long to rest, but as those who expect to "watch for the morning."

WHEN Godfrey Cass returned from Mrs. Osgood's party at midnight, he was not much surprised to learn that Dunsey had not come home. Perhaps he had not sold Wildfire, and was waiting for another chance; perhaps, on that foggy afternoon, he had preferred housing himself at the Red Lion at Batherley for the night, if the run had kept him in that neighborhood — for he was not likely to feel much concern about leaving his brother in suspense. Godfrey's mind was too full of Nancy Lammeter's looks and behavior, too full of the exasperation against himself and his lot which the sight of her always produced in him, for him to give much thought to Wildfire or to the probabilities of Dunstan's conduct.

The next morning, the whole village was excited by the story of the robbery, and Godfrey, like every one else, was occupied in gathering and discussing news about it and in visiting the Stone-pits. The rain had washed away all possibility of distinguishing footmarks, but a close investigation of the spot had disclosed, in the direction opposite to the village, a tinder box, with a flint and steel, half sunk in the mud. It was not Silas's tinder box, for the only one he had ever had was still standing on his shelf; and the inference generally accepted was that the tinder box in the ditch was somehow connected with the robbery. A small minority shook their heads, and intimated their opinion that it was not a robbery to have much light thrown on it by tinder boxes, that Master Marner's tale had a queer look with it, and that such things had been known as a man's doing himself a mischief and then setting the justice to look for the doer. But when questioned closely as to their grounds for this opinion, and what Master Marner had to gain by such false pretenses, they only shook their heads as before, and observed that there was no knowing what some folks counted gain ; moreover, that everybody had a right to their own opinions, grounds or no grounds, and that the weaver, as everybody knew, was partly crazy. Mr. Macey, though he joined in the defense of Marner against all suspicions of deceit, also pooh-poohed the tinder box ; indeed, repudiated it as a rather impious suggestion, tending to imply that everything must be done by human hands, and that there was no power which could make away with the guineas without moving the bricks. Nevertheless, he turned round rather sharply on Mr. Tookey, when the zealous deputy, feeling that this was a view of the case peculiarly suited to a parish clerk, carried it still further, and doubted whether it was right to inquire into a robbery at all when the circumstances were so mysterious.

"As if," concluded Mr. Tookey, "as if there was nothing but what could be made out by justices and constables."

"Now, don't you be for overshooting the mark, Tookey," said Mr. Macey, nodding his head aside admonishingly. "That 's what you 're allays at; if I throw a stone and hit, you think there 's summat better than hitting, and you try to throw a stone beyond. What I said was against the tinder box ; I said nothing against justices and constables, for they 're o' King George's making, and it 'ud be ill-becoming a man in a parish office to fly out again' King George."

While these discussions were going on amongst the group outside the Rainbow, a higher consultation was being carried on within, under the presidency of Mr. Crackenthorp, the rector, assisted by Squire Cass and other substantial parishioners. It had just occurred to Mr. Snell, the landlord — he being, as he observed, a man accustomed to put two and two together — to connect with the tinder box, which, as deputy constable, he himself had had the honorable distinction of finding, certain 5 recollections of a peddler who had called to drink at the house about a month before, and had actually stated that he carried a tinder box about with him to light his pipe. Here, surely, was a clue to be followed out. And as memory, when duly impregnated with ascertained facts, 10 is sometimes surprisingly fertile, Mr. Snell gradually recovered a vivid impression of the effect produced on him by the peddler's countenance and conversation. He had a "look with his eye" which fell unpleasantly on Mr. Snell's sensitive organism. To be sure, he did n't 15 say anything particular — no, except that about the tinder box; but it is n't what a man says, it 's the way he says it. Moreover, he had a swarthy foreignness of complexion which boded little honesty.

"Did he wear earrings?" Mr. Crackenthorp wished to 20 know, having some acquaintance with foreign customs.

"Well — stay — let me see," said Mr. Snell, like a docile clairvoyant who would really not make a mistake if she could help it. After stretching the corners of his mouth and contracting his eyes, as if he were trying to 25 see the earrings, he appeared to give up the effort, and said, "Well, he 'd got earrings in his box to sell, so it 's nat'ral to suppose he might wear 'em. But he called at every house, a'most, in the village; there 's somebody else, mayhap, saw 'em in his ears, though I can't take 30 upon me rightly to say."

Mr. Snell was correct in his surmise that somebody else would remember the peddler's earrings. For on the spread of inquiry among the villagers it was stated, with

gathering emphasis, that the parson had wanted to know whether the peddler wore earrings in his ears, and an impression was created that a great deal depended on the eliciting of this fact. Of course, every one who heard
5 the question, not having any distinct image of the peddler as *without* earrings, immediately had an image of him *with* earrings, larger or smaller, as the case might be; and the image was presently taken for a vivid recollection, so that the glazier's wife, a well-intentioned woman, not
10 given to lying, and whose house was among the cleanest in the village, was ready to declare, as sure as ever she meant to take the sacrament the very next Christmas that was ever coming, that she had seen big earrings, in the shape of the young moon, in the peddler's two ears; while
15 Jinny Oates, the cobbler's daughter, being a more imaginative person, stated not only that she had seen them, too, but that they had made her blood creep, as it did at that very moment while there she stood.

Also, by way of throwing further light on this clue of
20 the tinder box, a collection was made of all the articles purchased from the peddler at various houses and carried to the Rainbow to be exhibited there. In fact, there was a general feeling in the village that for the clearing up of this robbery there must be a great deal done at the
25 Rainbow, and that no man need offer his wife an excuse for going there while it was the scene of severe public duties.

Some disappointment was felt, and perhaps a little indignation, also, when it became known that Silas Mar-
30 ner, on being questioned by the Squire and the parson, had retained no other recollection of the peddler than that he had called at his door, but had not entered his house, having turned away at once when Silas, holding the door ajar, had said that he wanted nothing. This had been

Silas's testimony, though he clutched strongly at the idea of the peddler's being the culprit, if only because it gave him a definite image of a whereabout for his gold after it had been taken away from its hiding-place; he could see it now in the peddler's box. But it was observed with 5 some irritation in the village that anybody but a "blind creatur" like Marner would have seen the man prowling about, for how came he to leave his tinder box in the ditch close by if he hadn't been lingering there? Doubtless, he had made his observations when he saw Marner 10 at the door. Anybody might know — and only look at him — that the weaver was a half-crazy miser. It was a wonder the peddler hadn't murdered him; men of that sort, with rings in their ears, had been known for murderers often and often. There had been one tried at the 15 'sizes not so long ago but what there were people living who remembered it.

Godfrey Cass, indeed, entering the Rainbow during one of Mr. Snell's frequently repeated recitals of his testimony, had treated it lightly, stating that he himself 20 had bought a penknife of the peddler, and thought him a merry, grinning fellow enough; it was all nonsense, he said, about the man's evil looks. But this was spoken of in the village as the random talk of youth, "as if it was only Mr. Snell who had seen something odd about the 25 peddler!" On the contrary, there were at least half a dozen who were ready to go before Justice Malam and give in much more striking testimony than any the landlord could furnish. It was to be hoped Mr. Godfrey would not go to Tarley and throw cold water on what 30 Mr. Snell said there, and so prevent the justice from drawing up a warrant. He was suspected of intending this when, after midday, he was seen setting off on horseback in the direction of Tarley.

But by this time Godfrey's interest in the robbery had faded before his growing anxiety about Dunstan and Wildfire, and he was going, not to Tarley, but to Batherley, unable to rest in uncertainty about them any longer.
5 The possibility that Dunstan had played him the ugly trick of riding away with Wildfire, to return at the end of a month, when he had gambled away or otherwise squandered the price of the horse, was a fear that urged itself upon him more, even, than the thought of an accidental
10 injury; and now that the dance at Mrs. Osgood's was past he was irritated with himself that he had trusted his horse to Dunstan. Instead of trying to still his fears, he encouraged them, with that superstitious impression which clings to us all that if we expect evil very strongly
15 it is the less likely to come; and when he heard a horse approaching at a trot and saw a hat rising above a hedge beyond an angle of the lane he felt as if his conjuration had succeeded. But no sooner did the horse come within sight than his heart sank again. It was not
20 Wildfire, and in a few moments more he discerned that the rider was not Dunstan, but Bryce, who pulled up to speak, with a face that implied something disagreeable.

"Well, Mr. Godfrey, that's a lucky brother of yours, that Master Dunsey, is n't he?"

25 "What do you mean?" said Godfrey hastily.

"Why, has n't he been home yet?" said Bryce.

"Home? no. What has happened? Be quick. What has he done with my horse?"

"Ah, I thought it was yours, though he pretended you
30 had parted with it to him."

"Has he thrown him down and broken his knees?" said Godfrey, flushed with exasperation.

"Worse than that," said Bryce. "You see, I'd made a bargain with him to buy the horse for a hundred and twenty — a swinging price, but I always liked the horse. And what does he do but go and stake him — fly at a hedge with stakes in it, atop of a bank with a ditch before it. The horse had been dead a pretty good while when he was found. So he has n't been home since, has he?" 5

"Home? no," said Godfrey, "and he'd better keep away. Confound me for a fool! I might have known this would be the end of it."

"Well, to tell you the truth," said Bryce, "after I'd bargained for the horse, it did come into my head that 10 he might be riding and selling the horse without your knowledge, for I did n't believe it was his own. I knew Master Dunsey was up to his tricks sometimes. But where can he be gone? He's never been seen at Bath-erley. He could n't have been hurt, for he must have 15 walked off."

"Hurt?" said Godfrey bitterly. "He'll never be hurt — he's made to hurt other people."

"And so you *did* give him leave to sell the horse, eh?" said Bryce. 20

"Yes; I wanted to part with the horse — he was always a little too hard in the mouth for me," said Godfrey, his pride making him wince under the idea that Bryce guessed the sale to be a matter of necessity. "I was going to see after him — I thought some mischief had 25 happened. I'll go back now," he added, turning the horse's head and wishing he could get rid of Bryce; for he felt that the long-dreaded crisis in his life was close upon him. "You're coming on to Raveloe, are n't you?"

"Well, no, not now," said Bryce. "I *was* coming 30 round there, for I had to go to Flitton, and I thought I might as well take you in my way, and just let you know all I knew myself about the horse. I suppose Master Dunsey did n't like to show himself till the ill news had

blown over a bit.   He's perhaps gone to pay a visit at
the Three Crowns, by Whitbridge — I know he's fond of
the house."

   "Perhaps he is," said Godfrey, rather absently.   Then,
5 rousing himself, he said, with an effort at carelessness,
"We shall hear of him soon enough, I'll be bound."

   "Well, here's my turning," said Bryce, not surprised
to perceive that Godfrey was rather "down"; "so I'll
bid you good-day, and wish I may bring you better news
10 another time."

   Godfrey rode along slowly, representing to himself the
scene of confession to his father from which he felt that
there was now no longer any escape.   The revelation
about the money must be made the very next morning;
15 and if he withheld the rest, Dunstan would be sure to
come back shortly, and, finding that he must bear the
brunt of his father's anger, would tell the whole story out
of spite, even though he had nothing to gain by it.   There
was one step, perhaps, by which he might still win Dun-
20 stan's silence and put off the evil day : he might tell his
father that he had himself spent the money paid to him
by Fowler; and, as he had never been guilty of such an
offense before, the affair would blow over after a little
storming.   But Godfrey could not bend himself to this.
25 He felt that in letting Dunstan have the money he had
already been guilty of a breach of trust hardly less
culpable than that of spending the money directly for his
own behoof ; and yet there was a distinction between the
two acts which made him feel that the one was so much
30 more blackening than the other as to be intolerable to him.

   "I don't pretend to be a good fellow," he said to himself ; "but I'm not a scoundrel — at least, I'll stop short
somewhere.   I'll bear the consequences of what I *have*
done sooner than make believe I've done what I never

would have done. I'd never have spent the money for my own pleasure — I was tortured into it."

Through the remainder of this day Godfrey, with only occasional fluctuations, kept his will bent in the direction of a complete avowal to his father, and he withheld the story of Wildfire's loss till the next morning, that it might serve him as an introduction to heavier matter. The old Squire was accustomed to his son's frequent absence from home, and thought neither Dunstan's nor Wildfire's non-appearance a matter calling for remark. Godfrey said to himself again and again that if he let slip this one opportunity of confession he might never have another; the revelation might be made even in a more odious way than by Dunstan's malignity: *she* might come as she had threatened to do. And then he tried to make the scene easier to himself by rehearsal; he made up his mind how he would pass from the admission of his weakness in letting Dunstan have the money to the fact that Dunstan had a hold on him which he had been unable to shake off, and how he would work up his father to expect something very bad before he told him the fact. The old Squire was an implacable man; he made resolutions in violent anger, and he was not to be moved from them after his anger had subsided — as fiery volcanic matters cool and harden into rock. Like many violent and implacable men, he allowed evils to grow under favor of his own heedlessness, till they pressed upon him with exasperating force, and then he turned round with fierce severity and became unrelentingly hard. This was his system with his tenants; he allowed them to get into arrears, neglect their fences, reduce their stock, sell their straw, and otherwise go the wrong way — and then, when he became short of money in consequence of this indulgence, he took the hardest measures and would listen to no appeal. Godfrey knew all this, and felt it with the greater force because he had constantly suffered annoyance from witnessing his father's sudden fits of unrelentingness, for which his own habitual irresolution deprived him of all sympathy. (He was not critical on the faulty indulgence which preceded these fits; *that* seemed to him natural enough.) Still, there was just the chance, Godfrey thought, that his father's pride might see this marriage in a light that would induce him to hush it up, rather than turn his son out and make the family the talk of the country for ten miles round.

This was the view of the case that Godfrey managed to keep before him pretty closely till midnight, and he went to sleep thinking that he had done with inward debating. But when he awoke in the still morning darkness he found it impossible to reawaken his evening thoughts; it was as if they had been tired out and were not to be roused to further work. Instead of arguments for confession, he could now feel the presence of nothing but its evil consequences; the old dread of disgrace came back — the old shrinking from the thought of raising a hopeless barrier between himself and Nancy — the old disposition to rely on chances which might be favorable to him and save him from betrayal. Why, after all, should he cut off the hope of them by his own act? He had seen the matter in a wrong light yesterday. He had been in a rage with Dunstan, and had thought of nothing but a thorough breakup of their mutual understanding; but what it would be really wisest for him to do was to try and soften his father's anger against Dunsey and keep things as nearly as possible in their old condition. If Dunsey did not come back for a few days (and Godfrey did not know but that the rascal had enough money in his pocket to enable him to keep away still longer), everything might blow over.

CHAPTER IX.

GODFREY rose and took his own breakfast earlier than usual, but lingered in the wainscoted parlor till his younger brothers had finished their meal and gone out, awaiting his father, who always took a walk with his managing man before breakfast. Every one breakfasted at 5 a different hour in the Red House, and the Squire was always the latest, giving a long chance to a rather feeble morning appetite before he tried it. The table had been spread with substantial eatables nearly two hours before he presented himself, — a tall, stout man of sixty, with a face 10 in which the knit brow and rather hard glance seemed contradicted by the slack and feeble mouth. His person showed marks of habitual neglect, his dress was slovenly ; and yet there was something in the presence of the old Squire distinguishable from that of the ordinary farmers 15 in the parish, who were perhaps every whit as refined as he, but, having slouched their way through life with a consciousness of being in the vicinity of their "betters," wanted that self-possession and authoritativeness of voice and carriage which belonged to a man who thought of su- 20 periors as remote existences with whom he had personally little more to do than with America or the stars. The Squire had been used to parish homage all his life, used to the presupposition that his family, his tankards, and everything that was his were the oldest and best ; and, as he 25 never associated with any gentry higher than himself, his opinion was not disturbed by comparison.

He glanced at his son as he entered the room, and said, "What, sir ! have n't *you* had your breakfast yet?" but there was no pleasant morning greeting between them; not because of any unfriendliness, but because the sweet flower of courtesy is not a growth of such homes as the Red House.

5　　"Yes, sir," said Godfrey, "I 've had my breakfast, but I was waiting to speak to you."

"Ah! well," said the Squire, throwing himself indifferently into his chair, and speaking in a ponderous coughing fashion, which was felt in Raveloe to be a sort of privilege 10 of his rank, while he cut a piece of beef and held it up before the deerhound that had come in with him. "Ring the bell for my ale, will you? You youngsters' business is your own pleasure, mostly. There 's no hurry about it for anybody but yourselves."

15　The Squire's life was quite as idle as his sons', but it was a fiction kept up by himself and his contemporaries in Raveloe that youth was exclusively the period of folly, and that their aged wisdom was constantly in a state of endurance mitigated by sarcasm. Godfrey waited, before he 20 spoke again, until the ale had been brought and the door closed — an interval during which Fleet, the deerhound, had consumed enough bits of beef to make a poor man's holiday dinner.

"There 's been a cursed piece of ill luck with Wildfire," 25 he began; "happened the day before yesterday."

"What! broke his knees?" said the Squire, after taking a draught of ale. "I thought you knew how to ride better than that, sir. I never threw a horse down in my life. If I had, I might ha' whistled for another, for *my* 30 father was n't quite so ready to unstring as some other fathers I know of. But they must turn over a new leaf — *they* must. What with mortgages and arrears, I 'm as short o' cash as a roadside pauper. And that fool Kimble says the newspaper 's talking about peace. Why, the country would n't have a leg to stand on. Prices 'ud run down like a jack, and I should never get my arrears, not if I sold all the fellows up. And there 's that damned Fowler, I won't put up with him any longer ; I 've told Winthrop to go to Cox this very day. The lying scoun- 5 drel told me he 'd be sure to pay me a hundred last month. He takes advantage because he 's on that outlying farm, and thinks I shall forget him."

The Squire had delivered this speech in a coughing and interrupted manner, but with no pause long enough for 10 Godfrey to make it a pretext for taking up the word again. He felt that his father meant to ward off any request for money on the ground of the misfortune with Wildfire, and that the emphasis he had thus been led to lay on his shortness of cash and his arrears was likely to produce 15 an attitude of mind the utmost unfavorable for his own disclosure. But he must go on, now he had begun.

" It 's worse than breaking the horse's knees — he 's been staked and killed," he said, as soon as his father was silent and had begun to cut his meat. " But I was n't 20 thinking of asking you to buy me another horse ; I was only thinking I 'd lost the means of paying you with the price of Wildfire, as I 'd meant to do. Dunsey took him to the hunt to sell him for me the other day, and after he 'd made a bargain for a hundred and twenty with Bryce he 25 went after the hounds and took some fool 's leap or other that did for the horse at once. If it had n't been for that, I should have paid you a hundred pounds this morning."

The Squire had laid down his knife and fork and was staring at his son in amazement, not being sufficiently 30 quick of brain to form a probable guess as to what could have caused so strange an inversion of the paternal and filial relations as this proposition of his son to pay him a hundred pounds.

"The truth is, sir — I 'm very sorry — I was quite to blame," said Godfrey. "Fowler did pay that hundred pounds. He paid it to me when I was over there one day last month. And Dunsey bothered me for the money, and
5 I let him have it, because I hoped I should be able to pay it you before this."

The Squire was purple with anger before his son had done speaking, and found utterance difficult. "You let Dunsey have it, sir? And how long have you been so
10 thick with Dunsey that you must *collogue* with him to embezzle my money? Are you turning out a scamp? I tell you I won't have it. I 'll turn the whole pack of you out of the house together and marry again. I 'd have you to remember, sir, my property 's got no entail on it;
15 since my grandfather 's time the Casses can do as they like with their land. Remember that, sir. Let Dunsey have the money! Why should you let Dunsey have the money? There 's some lie at the bottom of it."

"There 's no lie, sir," said Godfrey. "I would n't have
20 spent the money myself; but Dunsey bothered me, and I was a fool and let him have it. But I meant to pay it, whether he did or not. That 's the whole story. I never meant to embezzle money, and I 'm not the man to do it. You never knew me do a dishonest trick, sir."

25 "Where 's Dunsey, then? What do you stand talking there for? Go and fetch Dunsey, as I tell you, and let him give account of what he wanted the money for and what he 's done with it. He shall repent it. I 'll turn him out. I said I would, and I 'll do it. He sha'n't brave me.
30 Go and fetch him."

"Dunsey is n't come back, sir."

"What! did he break his own neck, then?" said the Squire, with some disgust at the idea that, in that case, he could not fulfill his threat.

" No, he was n't hurt, I believe, for the horse was found dead, and Dunsey must have walked off. I daresay we shall see him again by and by. I don't know where he is."

" And what must you be letting him have my money for? Answer me that," said the Squire, attacking God- 5 frey again, since Dunsey was not within reach.

" Well, sir, I don't know," said Godfrey hesitatingly. That was a feeble evasion, but Godfrey was not fond of lying, and, not being sufficiently aware that no sort of duplicity can long flourish without the help of vocal false- 10 hoods, he was quite unprepared with invented motives.

" You don't know? I tell you what it is, sir. You've been up to some trick, and you 've been bribing him not to tell," said the Squire, with a sudden acuteness which startled Godfrey, who felt his heart beat violently at the 15 nearness of his father's guess. The sudden alarm pushed him on to take the next step — a very slight impulse suf- fices for that on a downward road.

" Why, sir," he said, trying to speak with careless ease, " it was a little affair between me and Dunsey; it 's no 20 matter to anybody else. It 's hardly worth while to pry into young men's fooleries; it would n't have made any difference to you, sir, if I 'd not had the bad luck to lose Wildfire. I should have paid you the money."

" Fooleries! Pshaw! it 's time you 'd done with fooleries. 25 And I 'd have you know, sir, you *must* ha' done with 'em," said the Squire, frowning and casting an angry glance at his son. " Your goings-on are not what I shall find money for any longer. There 's my grandfather had his stables full o' horses, and kept a good house, too, and in worse 30 times, by what I can make out; and so might I, if I had n't four good-for-nothing fellows to hang on me like horse leeches. I 've been too good a father to you all — that 's what it is. But I shall pull up, sir."

Godfrey was silent. He was not likely to be very pene-
trating in his judgments, but he had always had a sense
that his father's indulgence had not been kindness, and
had had a vague longing for some discipline that would
5 have checked his own errant weakness and helped his
better will. The Squire ate his bread and meat hastily,
took a deep draught of ale, then turned his chair from
the table, and began to speak again.

"It 'll be all the worse for you, you know — you 'd need
10 try and help me keep things together."

"Well, sir, I 've often offered to take the management
of things, but you know you 've taken it ill always, and
seemed to think I wanted to push you out of your
place."

15 "I know nothing o' your offering or o' my taking it
ill," said the Squire, whose memory consisted in certain
strong impressions unmodified by detail; "but I know
one while you seemed to be thinking o' marrying, and I
did n't offer to put any obstacles in your way, as some
20 fathers would. I 'd as lieve you married Lammeter's
daughter as anybody. I suppose if I 'd said you nay
you 'd ha' kept on with it; but, for want o' contradiction,
you 've changed your mind. You 're a shilly-shally fellow;
you take after your poor mother. She never had a will of
25 her own; a woman has no call for one, if she 's got a
proper man for her husband. But *your* wife had need
have one, for you hardly know your own mind enough to
make both your legs walk one way. The lass has n't said
downright she won't have you, has she?"

30 "No," said Godfrey, feeling very hot and uncomfortable; "but I don't think she will."

"Think! why have n't you the courage to ask her?
Do you stick to it you want to have *her* — that 's the
thing?"

" There 's no other woman I want to marry," said Godfrey evasively.

" Well, then, let me make the offer for you, that 's all,
if you have n't the pluck to do it yourself. Lammeter
is n't likely to be loath for his daughter to marry into *my*
family, I should think. And as for the pretty lass, she
would n't have her cousin ; and there 's nobody else, as I
see, could ha' stood in your way."

" I 'd rather let it be, please, sir, at present," said Godfrey in alarm. " I think she 's a little offended with me
just now, and I should like to speak for myself. A man
must manage these things for himself."

" Well, speak, then, and manage it, and see if you can't
turn over a new leaf. That 's what a man must do when
he thinks o' marrying."

" I don't see how I can think of it at present, sir. You
would n't like to settle me on one of the farms, I suppose,
and I don't think she 'd come to live in this house with all
my brothers. It 's a different sort of life to what she 's
been used to."

" Not come to live in this house? Don't tell me. You
ask her, that 's all," said the Squire, with a short, scornful
laugh.

" I 'd rather let the thing be at present, sir," said Godfrey. " I hope you won't try to hurry it on by saying
anything."

" I shall do what I choose," said the Squire, "and I
shall let you know I 'm master ; else you may turn out, and
find an estate to drop into somewhere else. Go out and
tell Winthrop not to go to Cox's, but wait for me. And
tell 'em to get my horse saddled. And stop — look out
and get that hack o' Dunsey's sold, and hand me the
money, will you? He 'll keep no more hacks at my
expense. And if you know where he 's sneaking — I

daresay you do — you may tell him to spare himself the journey o' coming back home. Let him turn ostler, and keep himself. He sha'n't hang on me any more."

"I don't know where he is ; and if I did, it is n't my place to tell him to keep away," said Godfrey, moving towards the door.

"Confound it, sir, don't stay arguing, but go and order my horse," said the Squire, taking up a pipe.

Godfrey left the room, hardly knowing whether he were more relieved by the sense that the interview was ended without having made any change in his position or more uneasy that he had entangled himself still further in prevarication and deceit. What had passed about his proposing to Nancy had raised a new alarm, lest by some after-dinner words of his father's to Mr. Lammeter he should be thrown into the embarrassment of being obliged absolutely to decline her when she seemed to be within his reach. He fled to his usual refuge, that of hoping for some unforeseen turn of fortune, some favorable chance which would save him from unpleasant consequences — perhaps even justify his insincerity by manifesting its prudence.

In this point of trusting to some throw of fortune's dice, Godfrey can hardly be called old-fashioned. Favorable Chance is the god of all men who follow their own devices instead of obeying a law they believe in. Let even a polished man of these days get into a position he is ashamed to avow, and his mind will be bent on all the possible issues that may deliver him from the calculable results of that position. Let him live outside his income or shirk the resolute honest work that brings wages, and he will presently find himself dreaming of a possible benefactor, a possible simpleton who may be cajoled into using his interest, a possible state of mind in some possible person not yet forthcoming. Let him neglect the responsibilities of his office, and he will inevitably anchor himself on the chance that the thing left undone may turn out not to be of the supposed importance. Let him betray his friend's confidence, and he will adore that same cunning complexity 5 called Chance, which gives him the hope that his friend will never know. Let him forsake a decent craft that he may pursue the gentilities of a profession to which nature never called him, and his religion will infallibly be the worship of blessed Chance, which he will believe in as the 10 mighty creator of success. The evil principle deprecated in that religion is the orderly sequence by which the seed brings forth a crop after its kind.

CHAPTER X.

JUSTICE MALAM was naturally regarded in Tarley and Raveloe as a man of capacious mind, seeing that he could draw much wider conclusions without evidence than could be expected of his neighbors who were not on the Com-
5 mission of the Peace. Such a man was not likely to neglect the clue of the tinder box, and an inquiry was set on foot concerning a peddler, name unknown, with curly black hair and a foreign complexion, carrying a box of cutlery and jewelry and wearing large rings in his ears.
10 But, either because inquiry was too slow-footed to over-take him or because the description applied to so many peddlers that inquiry did not know how to choose among them, weeks passed away, and there was no other result concerning the robbery than a gradual cessation of the ex-
15 citement it had caused in Raveloe. Dunstan Cass's ab-sence was hardly a subject of remark ; he had once before had a quarrel with his father, and had gone off, nobody knew whither, to return at the end of six weeks, take up his old quarters unforbidden, and swagger as usual. His
20 own family, who equally expected this issue, with the sole difference that the Squire was determined this time to forbid him the old quarters, never mentioned his absence ; and when his Uncle Kimble or Mr. Osgood noticed it, the story of his having killed Wildfire and committed some
25 offense against his father was enough to prevent surprise. To connect the fact of Dunsey's disappearance with that of the robbery occurring on the same day lay quite away from the track of every one's thought — even Godfrey's, who had better reason than any one else to know what

his brother was capable of. He remembered no mention of the weaver between them since the time, twelve years ago, when it was their boyish sport to deride him ; and, besides, his imagination constantly created an *alibi* for Dunstan. He saw him continually in some congenial haunt, to which he had walked off on leaving Wildfire, saw him sponging on chance acquaintances and meditating a return home to the old amusement of tormenting his elder brother. Even if any brain in Raveloe had put the said two facts together, I doubt whether a combination so injurious to the prescriptive respectability of a family with a mural monument and venerable tankards would not have been suppressed as of unsound tendency. But Christmas puddings, brawn, and abundance of spirituous liquors, throwing the mental originality into the channel of nightmare, are great preservatives against a dangerous spontaneity of waking thought.

When the robbery was talked of at the Rainbow and elsewhere, in good company, the balance continued to waver between the rational explanation founded on the tinder box and the theory of an impenetrable mystery that mocked investigation. The advocates of the tinder box and peddler view considered the other side a muddleheaded and credulous set, who, because they themselves were wall-eyed, supposed everybody else to have the same blank outlook ; and the adherents of the inexplicable more than hinted that their antagonists were animals inclined to crow before they had found any corn, — mere skimming dishes in point of depth, — whose clear-sightedness consisted in supposing there was nothing behind a barn door because they couldn't see through it; so that, though their controversy did not serve to elicit the fact concerning the robbery, it elicited some true opinions of collateral importance.

But, while poor Silas's loss served thus to brush the slow current of Raveloe conversation, Silas himself was feeling the withering desolation of that bereavement about which his neighbors were arguing at their ease. To any one who had observed him before he lost his gold, it might have seemed that so withered and shrunken a life as his could hardly be susceptible of a bruise, could hardly endure any subtraction but such as would put an end to it altogether. But in reality it had been an eager life, filled with immediate purpose which fenced him in from the wide, cheerless unknown. It had been a clinging life; and though the object round which its fibers had clung was a dead, disrupted thing, it satisfied the need for clinging. But now the fence was broken down — the support was snatched away. Marner's thoughts could no longer move in their old round, and were baffled by a blank like that which meets a plodding ant when the earth has broken away on its homeward path. The loom was there, and the weaving, and the growing pattern in the cloth; but the bright treasure in the hole under his feet was gone; the prospect of handling and counting it was gone; the evening had no phantasm of delight to still the poor soul's craving. The thought of the money he would get by his actual work could bring no joy, for its meager image was only a fresh reminder of his loss; and hope was too heavily crushed by the sudden blow for his imagination to dwell on the growth of a new hoard from that small beginning.

He filled up the blank with grief. As he sat weaving, he every now and then moaned low, like one in pain; it was the sign that his thoughts had come round again to the sudden chasm — to the empty evening time. And all the evening, as he sat in his loneliness by his dull fire, he leaned his elbows on his knees and clasped his head with

his hands, and moaned very low — not as one who seeks
to be heard.

And yet he was not utterly forsaken in his trouble. The
repulsion Marner had always created in his neighbors
was partly dissipated by the new light in which this mis-   5
fortune had shown him. Instead of a man who had more
cunning than honest folks could come by, and, what was
worse, had not the inclination to use that cunning in a
neighborly way, it was now apparent that Silas had not
cunning enough to keep his own. He was generally   10
spoken of as a " poor, mushed creatur " ; and that avoid-
ance of his neighbors, which had before been referred to
his ill will and to a probable addiction to worse company,
was now considered mere craziness.

This change to a kindlier feeling was shown in various   15
ways. The odor of Christmas cooking being on the wind,
it was the season when superfluous pork and black puddings are suggestive of charity in well-to-do families ; and
Silas's misfortune had brought him uppermost in the
memory of housekeepers like Mrs. Osgood. Mr. Cracken-   20
thorp, too, while he admonished Silas that his money had
probably been taken from him because he thought too
much of it and never came to church, enforced the doctrine
by a present of pigs' pettitoes, well calculated to dissipate
unfounded prejudices against the clerical character. Neigh-   25
bors who had nothing but verbal consolation to give
showed a disposition not only to greet Silas and discuss
his misfortune at some length when they encountered him
in the village, but also to take the trouble of calling at his
cottage and getting him to repeat all the details on the   30
very spot ; and then they would try to cheer him by saying, " Well, Master Marner, you 're no worse off nor other
poor folks, after all ; and if you was to be crippled, the
parish 'ud give you a 'lowance."

I suppose one reason why we are seldom able to comfort our neighbors with our words is that our good will
gets adulterated, in spite of ourselves, before it can pass
our lips. We can send black puddings and pettitoes
5 without giving them a flavor of our own egoism; but
language is a stream that is almost sure to smack of a
mingled soil. There was a fair proportion of kindness in
Raveloe ; but it was often of a beery and bungling sort,
and took the shape least allied to the complimentary and
10 hypocritical.

Mr. Macey, for example, coming one evening expressly
to let Silas know that recent events had given him the
advantage of standing more favorably in the opinion of
a man whose judgment was not formed lightly, opened
15 the conversation by saying, as soon as he had seated
himself and adjusted his thumbs :

"Come, Master Marner, why, you've no call to sit
a-moaning. You're a deal better off to ha' lost your
money, nor to ha' kep it by foul means. I used to think,
20 when you first come into these parts, as you were no
better nor you should be; you were younger a deal than
what you are now, but you were allays a staring, white-
faced creatur, partly like a bald-faced calf, as I may say.
But there's no knowing; it isn't every queer-looksed
25 thing as Old Harry's had the making of, — I mean,
speaking o' toads and such, — for they're often harmless
and useful against varmin. And it's pretty much the
same wi' you, as fur as I can see. Though as to the
yarbs and stuff to cure the breathing, if you brought that
30 sort o' knowledge from distant parts, you might ha' been
a bit freer of it. And if the knowledge wasn't well come
by, why, you might ha' made up for it by coming to
church reg'lar; for, as for the children as the Wise
Woman charmed, I've been at the christening of 'em

again and again, and they took the water just as well.
And that's reasonable; for if Old Harry's a mind to do
a bit o' kindness for a holiday, like, who's got anything
against it?   That's my thinking; and I've been clerk o'
this parish forty year, and I know, when the parson and   5
me does the cussing of a Ash Wednesday, there's no
cussing o' folks as have a mind to be cured without a
doctor, let Kimble say what he will.   An so, Master
Marner, as I was saying, — for there's windings i' things
as they may carry you to the fur end o' the prayer-book 10
afore you get back to 'em, — my advice is as you keep up
your sperrits; for, as for thinking you're a deep un and
ha' got more inside you nor 'ull bear daylight, I'm not
o' that opinion at all, and so I tell the neighbors.   For,
says I, you talk o' Master Marner making out a tale, — 15
why, it's nonsense, that is; it 'ud take a 'cute man to
make a tale like that, and, says I, he looked as scared
as a rabbit."

During this discursive address Silas had continued motionless in his previous attitude, leaning his elbows on 20
his knees and pressing his hands against his head.   Mr.
Macey, not doubting that he had been listened to, paused,
in the expectation of some appreciatory reply; but Marner
remained silent.   He had a sense that the old man
meant to be good natured and neighborly; but the kind- 25
ness fell on him as sunshine falls on the wretched — he had
no heart to taste it, and felt that it was very far off him.

"Come, Master Marner, have you got nothing to say
to that?" said Mr. Macey at last, with a slight accent of
impatience.   30

"Oh," said Marner slowly, shaking his head between
his hands, "I thank you — thank you — kindly."

"Ay, ay, to be sure; I thought you would," said Mr.
Macey; "and my advise is — have you got a Sunday suit?"

"No," said Marner.

"I doubted it was so," said Mr. Macey. "Now, let me advise you to get a Sunday suit. There's Tookey, he's a poor creatur, but he's got my tailoring business, and some o' my money in it, and he shall make a suit at a low price and give you trust, and then you can come to church and be a bit neighborly. Why, you've never heared me say 'Amen' since you come into these parts, and I recommend you to lose no time, for it'll be poor work when Tookey has it all to himself, for I mayn't be equil to stand i' the desk at all come another winter." Here Mr. Macey paused, perhaps expecting some sign of emotion in his hearer; but, not observing any, he went on. "And as for the money for the suit o' clothes, why, you get a matter of a pound a week at your weaving, Master Marner, and you're a young man, eh, for all you look so mushed. Why, you couldn't ha' been five and twenty when you come into these parts, eh?"

Silas started a little at the change to a questioning tone, and answered mildly, "I don't know; I can't rightly say — it's a long while since."

After receiving such an answer as this, it is not surprising that Mr. Macey observed, later on in the evening at the Rainbow, that Marner's head was "all of a muddle," and that it was to be doubted if he ever knew when Sunday come round, which showed him a worse heathen than many a dog.

Another of Silas's comforters, besides Mr. Macey, came to him with a mind highly charged on the same topic. This was Mrs. Winthrop, the wheelwright's wife. The inhabitants of Raveloe were not severely regular in their church going, and perhaps there was hardly a person in the parish who would not have held that to go to church every Sunday in the calendar would have shown a greedy

desire to stand well with Heaven and get an undue
advantage over their neighbors, — a wish to be better
than the "common run," that would have implied a
reflection on those who had had godfathers and god-
mothers as well as themselves, and had an equal right to
the burying service. At the same time, it was understood
to be requisite for all who were not household servants or
young men to take the sacrament at one of the great
festivals. Squire Cass himself took it on Christmas Day;
while those who were held to be "good livers" went to
church with greater, though still with moderate, frequency.

Mrs. Winthrop was one of these; she was in all re-
spects a woman of scrupulous conscience, so eager for
duties that life seemed to offer them too scantily unless
she rose at half past four, though this threw a scarcity of
work over the more advanced hours of the morning which
it was a constant problem with her to remove. Yet she
had not the vixenish temper which is sometimes supposed
to be a necessary condition of such habits; she was a
very mild, patient woman, whose nature it was to seek
out all the sadder and more serious elements of life and
pasture her mind upon them. She was the person always
first thought of in Raveloe when there was illness or
death in the family, when leeches were to be applied, or
there was a sudden disappointment in a monthly nurse.
She was a "comfortable woman," good-looking, fresh-
complexioned, having her lips always slightly screwed, as
if she felt herself in a sick room with a doctor or the
clergyman present. But she was never whimpering, no
one had seen her shed tears; she was simply grave and
inclined to shake her head and sigh, almost imperceptibly,
like a funereal mourner who is not a relation. It seemed
surprising that Ben Winthrop, who loved his quart-pot
and his joke, got along so well with Dolly; but she took

her husband's jokes and joviality as patiently as everything else, considering that "men *would* be so," and
viewing the stronger sex in the light of animals whom it
had pleased Heaven to make naturally troublesome, like
5 bulls and turkey cocks.

This good, wholesome woman could hardly fail to have
her mind drawn strongly towards Silas Marner, now that
he appeared in the light of a sufferer ; and one Sunday
afternoon she took her little boy Aaron with her and
10 went to call on Silas, carrying in her hand some small
lard cakes, flat, paste-like articles much esteemed in
Raveloe. Aaron, an apple-cheeked youngster of seven,
with a clean starched frill which looked like a plate for
the apples, needed all his adventurous curiosity to em-
15 bolden him against the possibility that the big-eyed weaver
might do him some bodily injury ; and his dubiety was
much increased when, on arriving at the Stone-pits, they
heard the mysterious sound of the loom.

"Ah, it is as I thought," said Mrs. Winthrop sadly.

20 They had to knock loudly before Silas heard them ; but
when he did come to the door he showed no impatience, as
he would once have done, at a visit that had been unasked
for and unexpected. Formerly, his heart had been as a
locked casket with its treasure inside ; but now the casket
25 was empty and the lock was broken. Left groping in
darkness, with his prop utterly gone, Silas had inevitably
a sense, though a dull and half-despairing one, that if any
help came to him it must come from without ; and there
was a slight stirring of expectation at the sight of his
30 fellow-men, a faint consciousness of dependence on their
good will. He opened the door wide to admit Dolly, but
without otherwise returning her greeting than by moving
the armchair a few inches as a sign that she was to sit
down in it. Dolly, as soon as she was seated, removed

the white cloth that covered her lard cakes, and said in her gravest way :

"I'd a baking yisterday, Master Marner, and the lard cakes turned out better nor common, and I'd ha' asked you to accept some, if you'd thought well. I don't eat 5 such things myself, for a bit o' bread's what I like from one year's end to the other ; but men's stomichs are made so comical, they want a change — they do, I know, God help 'em."

Dolly sighed gently as she held out the cakes to Silas, 10 who thanked her kindly and looked very close at them, absently, being accustomed to look so at everything he took into his hand — eyed all the while by the wondering, bright orbs of the small Aaron, who had made an outwork of his mother's chair, and was peeping round from be- 15 hind it.

"There's letters pricked on 'em," said Dolly. "I can't read 'em myself, and there's nobody, not Mr. Macey himself, rightly knows what they mean ; but they've a good meaning, for they're the same as is on the pulpit cloth at 20 church. What are they, Aaron, my dear?"

Aaron retreated completely behind his outwork.

"Oh, go, that's naughty," said his mother mildly. "Well, whativer the letters are, they've a good meaning ; and it's a stamp as has been in our house, Ben says, ever 25 since he was a little un, and his mother used to put it on the cakes, and I've allays put it on, too ; for if there's any good, we've need of it i' this world."

"It's I. H. S.," said Silas, at which proof of learning Aaron peeped round the chair again. 30

"Well, to be sure, you can read 'em off," said Dolly. "Ben's read 'em to me many and many a time, but they slip out o' my mind again — the more's the pity, for they're good letters, else they wouldn't be in the church;

and so I prick 'em on all the loaves and all the cakes,
though sometimes they won't hold, because o' the rising —
for, as I said, if there 's any good to be got we 've need
of it i' this world — that we have. And I hope they 'll
5 bring good to you, Master Marner, for it 's wi' that will I
brought you the cakes ; and you see the letters have held
better nor common."

Silas was as unable to interpret the letters as Dolly, but
there was no possibility of misunderstanding the desire to
10 give comfort that made itself heard in her quiet tones.
He said, with more feeling than before, "Thank you —
thank you kindly." But he laid down the cakes and
seated himself absently, drearily unconscious of any distinct benefit towards which the cakes and the letters, or
15 even Dolly's kindness, could tend for him.

"Ah, if there 's good anywhere, we 've need of it," repeated Dolly, who did not lightly forsake a serviceable
phrase. She looked at Silas pityingly as she went on.
"But you did n't hear the church bells this morning,
20 Master Marner ? I doubt you did n't know it was Sunday.
Living so lone here, you lose your count, I daresay ; and
then when your loom makes a noise you can't hear the
bells, more partic'lar now the frost kills the sound."

"Yes, I did ; I heard 'em," said Silas, to whom Sunday
25 bells were a mere accident of the day, and not part of its
sacredness. There had been no bells in Lantern Yard.

"Dear heart !" said Dolly, pausing before she spoke
again. "But what a pity it is you should work of a
Sunday, and not clean yourself — if you *did n't* go to
30 church ; for if you 'd a roasting bit, it might be as you
could n't leave it, being a lone man. But there 's the
bakehus, if you could make up your mind to spend a two-
pence on the oven now and then — not every week, in
course — I should n't like to do that myself — you might

carry your bit o' dinner there, for it 's nothing but right
to have a bit o' summat hot of a Sunday, and not to make
it as you can't know your dinner from Saturday. But
now, upo' Christmas Day, this blessed Christmas as is ever
coming, if you was to take your dinner to the bakehus 5
and go to church and see the holly and the yew and hear
the anthim and then take the sacramen' you 'd be a deal
the better, and you 'd know which end you stood on, and
you could put your trust i' Them as knows better nor we
do, seein' you 'd ha' done what it lies on us all to do." 10

Dolly's exhortation, which was an unusually long effort
of speech for her, was uttered in the soothing persuasive
tone with which she would have tried to prevail on a sick
man to take his medicine or a basin of gruel for which
he had no appetite. Silas had never before been closely 15
urged on the point of his absence from church, which had
only been thought of as a part of his general queerness;
and he was too direct and simple to evade Dolly's appeal.

" Nay, nay," he said, " I know nothing o' church. I 've
never been to church." 20

" No ! " said Dolly, in a low tone of wonderment. Then,
bethinking herself of Silas's advent from an unknown
country, she said, " Could it ha' been as they 'd no church
where you was born ? "

" Oh, yes," said Silas meditatively, sitting in his usual 25
posture of leaning on his knees and supporting his head.
" There was churches — a many — it was a big town. But
I know nothing of 'em — I went to chapel."

Dolly was much puzzled at this new word, but she was
rather afraid of inquiring further, lest " chapel " might 30
mean some haunt of wickedness. After a little thought,
she said :

" Well, Master Marner, it 's niver too late to turn over a
new leaf, and if you 've niver had no church there 's no

telling the good it 'll do you. For I feel so set up and comfortable as niver was when I 've been and heard the prayers and the singing to the praise and glory o' God, as Mr. Macey gives out, and Mr. Crackenthorp saying good
5 words, and more partic'lar on Sacramen' Day; and if a bit o' trouble comes I feel as I can put up wi' it, for I 've looked for help i' the right quarter and gev myself up to Them as we must all give ourselves up to at the last; and
· if we 'n done our part, it is n't to be believed as Them as
10 are above us 'ull be worse nor we are and come short o' Their 'n.

Poor Dolly's exposition of her simple Raveloe theology fell rather unmeaningly on Silas's ears, for there was no word in it that could rouse a memory of what he had
15 known as religion, and his comprehension was quite baffled by the plural pronoun, which was no heresy of Dolly's, but only her way of avoiding a presumptuous familiarity. He remained silent, not feeling inclined to assent to the part of Dolly's speech which he fully understood, — her
20 recommendation that he should go to church. Indeed, Silas was so unaccustomed to talk beyond the brief questions and answers necessary for the transaction of his simple business that words did not easily come to him without the urgency of a distinct purpose.
25 But now, little Aaron, having become used to the weaver's awful presence, had advanced to his mother's side, and Silas, seeming to notice him for the first time, tried to return Dolly's signs of good will by offering the lad a bit of lard cake. Aaron shrank back a little, and
30 rubbed his head against his mother's shoulder, but still thought the piece of cake worth the risk of putting his hand out for it.

"Oh, for shame, Aaron," said his mother, taking him on her lap, however; "why, you don't want cake again yet awhile.   He 's wonderful hearty," she went on, with a little sigh ; " that he is, God knows.   He 's my youngest, and we spoil him sadly, for either me or the father must allays hev him in our sight — that we must."

She stroked Aaron's brown head, and thought it must 5 do Master Marner good to see such a " pictur of a child." But Marner, on the other side of the hearth, saw the neat-featured, rosy face as a mere dim round, with two dark spots in it.

" And he 's got a voice like a bird — you would n't 10 think," Dolly went on ; " he can sing a Christmas carril as his father 's taught him; and I take it for a token as he 'll come to good, as he can learn the good tunes so quick.   Come, Aaron, stan' up and sing the carril to Master Marner, come." 15

Aaron replied by rubbing his forehead against his mother's shoulder.

" Oh, that 's naughty," said Dolly gently.   " Stan' up, when mother tells you, and let me hold the cake till you 've done." 20

Aaron was not indisposed to display his talents, even to an ogre, under protecting circumstances; and after a few more signs of coyness, consisting chiefly in rubbing the backs of his hands over his eyes and then peeping between them at Master Marner to see if he looked anxious for the 25 " carril," he at length allowed his head to be duly adjusted, and, standing behind the table, which let him appear above it only as far as his broad frill, so that he looked like a cherubic head untroubled with a body, he began with a clear chirp and in a melody that had the rhythm of 30 an industrious hammer :

> " God rest you, merry gentlemen,
>   Let nothing you dismay,
>   For Jesus Christ our Saviour
>   Was born on Christmas Day." 35

Dolly listened with a devout look, glancing at Marner in some confidence that this strain would help to allure him to church.

"That's Christmas music," she said, when Aaron had
5 ended and had secured his piece of cake again. "There's no other music equil to the Christmas music — 'Hark the erol angils sing.' And you may judge what it is at church, Master Marner, with the bassoon and the voices, as you can't help thinking you've got to a better place
10 a'ready — for I would n't speak ill o' this world, seeing as Them put us in it as knows best ; but what wi' the drink and the quarreling and the bad illnesses and the hard dying, as I've seen times and times, one's thankful to hear of a better. The boy sings pretty, don't he, Master
15 Marner ? "

"Yes," said Silas absently, "very pretty."

The Christmas carol, with its hammer-like rhythm, had fallen on his ears as strange music, quite unlike a hymn, and could have none of the effect Dolly contemplated.
20 But he wanted to show her that he was grateful, and the only mode that occurred to him was to offer Aaron a bit more cake.

"Oh, no, thank you, Master Marner," said Dolly, holding down Aaron's willing hands. "We must be going
25 home now. And so I wish you good-by, Master Marner ; and if you ever feel anyways bad in your inside, as you can't fend for yourself, I'll come and clean up for you and get you a bit o' victual, and willing. But I beg and pray of you to leave off weaving of a Sunday, for it's bad
30 for soul and body; and the money as comes i' that way 'ull be a bad bed to lie down on at the last, if it does n't fly away, nobody knows where, like the white frost. And you'll excuse me being that free with you, Master Marner, for I wish you well — I do. Make your bow, Aaron."

Silas said, "Good-by, and thank you kindly," as he opened the door for Dolly, but he could n't help feeling relieved when she was gone — relieved that he might weave again and moan at his ease. Her simple view of life and its comforts, by which she had tried to cheer him, was only like a report of unknown objects, which his imagination could not fashion. The fountains of human love and of faith in a divine love had not yet been unlocked, and his soul was still the shrunken rivulet, with only this difference, that its little groove of sand was blocked up, and it wandered confusedly against dark obstruction.

And so, notwithstanding the honest persuasions of Mr. Macey and Dolly Winthrop, Silas spent his Christmas Day in loneliness, eating his meat in sadness of heart, though the meat had come to him as a neighborly present. In the morning he looked out on the black frost that seemed to press cruelly on every blade of grass, while the half-icy red pool shivered under the bitter wind ; but towards evening the snow began to fall, and curtained from him even that dreary outlook, shutting him close up with his narrow grief. And he sat in his robbed home through the livelong evening, not caring to close his shutters or lock his door, pressing his head between his hands and moaning, till the cold grasped him and told him that his fire was gray.

Nobody in this world but himself knew that he was the same Silas Marner who had once loved his fellow with tender love and trusted in an unseen goodness. Even to himself that past experience had become dim.

But in Raveloe village the bells rang merrily, and the church was fuller than all through the rest of the year, with red faces among the abundant dark-green boughs — faces prepared for a longer service than usual by an odor-

ous breakfast of toast and ale. Those green boughs, the
hymn and anthem never heard but at Christmas, even the
Athanasian Creed — which was discriminated from the
others only as being longer and of exceptional virtue, since
5 it was only read on rare occasions — brought a vague
exulting sense, for which the grown men could as little
have found words as the children, that something great
and mysterious had been done for them in heaven above
and in earth below, which they were appropriating by
10 their presence. And then the red faces made their way
through the black biting frost to their own homes, feeling
themselves free for the rest of the day to eat, drink, and
be merry, and using that Christian freedom without diffi-
dence.

15 At Squire Cass's family party that day nobody mentioned Dunstan ; nobody was sorry for his absence or
feared it would be too long. The doctor and his wife,
Uncle and Aunt Kimble, were there, and the annual
Christmas talk was carried through without any omissions,
20 rising to the climax of Mr. Kimble's experience when he
walked the London hospitals thirty years back, together
with striking professional anecdotes then gathered. Whereupon cards followed, with Aunt Kimble's annual failure to
follow suit, and Uncle Kimble's irascibility concerning
25 the odd trick which was rarely explicable to him, when it
was not on his side, without a general visitation of tricks
to see that they were formed on sound principles, the
whole being accompanied by a strong steaming odor of
spirits and water.

30 But the party on Christmas Day, being a strictly family
party, was not the preëminently brilliant celebration of
the season at the Red House. It was the great dance on
New Year's Eve that made the glory of Squire Cass's hospitality, as of his forefathers', time out of mind. This

was the occasion when all the society of Raveloe and Tarley, whether old acquaintances separated by long, rutty distances, or cooled acquaintances separated by misunderstandings concerning runaway calves, or acquaintances founded on intermittent condescension, counted on meeting and on comporting themselves with mutual appropriateness. This was the occasion on which fair dames who came on pillions sent their bandboxes before them, supplied with more than their evening costume ; for the feast was not to end with a single evening, like a paltry town entertainment, where the whole supply of eatables is put on the table at once and bedding is scanty. The Red House was provisioned as if for a siege ; and as for the spare feather beds ready to be laid on floors, they were as plentiful as might naturally be expected in a family that had killed its own geese for many generations.

Godfrey Cass was looking forward to this New Year's Eve with a foolish, reckless longing that made him half deaf to his importunate companion, Anxiety.

"Dunsey will be coming home soon ; there will be a great blow-up, and how will you bribe his spite to silence?" said Anxiety.

"Oh, he won't come home before New Year's Eve, perhaps," said Godfrey ; "and I shall sit by Nancy then and dance with her and get a kind look from her, in spite of herself."

"But money is wanted in another quarter," said Anxiety in a louder voice, "and how will you get it without selling your mother's diamond pin ? And if you don't get it — ? "

"Well, but something may happen to make things easier. At any rate, there's one pleasure for me close at hand, — Nancy is coming."

"Yes, and suppose your father should bring matters to

a pass that will oblige you to decline marrying her — and to give your reasons?"

"Hold your tongue, and don't worry me. I can see Nancy's eyes, just as they will look at me, and feel her hand in mine already."

But Anxiety went on, though in noisy Christmas company, refusing to be utterly quieted even by much drinking.

CHAPTER XI.

SOME women, I grant, would not appear to advantage seated on a pillion and attired in a drab joseph and a drab beaver bonnet, with a crown resembling a small stew pan; for a garment suggesting a coachman's greatcoat, cut out under an exiguity of cloth that would only allow of 5 miniature capes, is not well adapted to conceal deficiencies of contour, nor is drab a color that will throw sallow cheeks into lively contrast. It was all the greater triumph to Miss Nancy Lammeter's beauty that she looked thoroughly bewitching in that costume, as, seated on the 10 pillion behind her tall, erect father, she held one arm round him, and looked down, with open-eyed anxiety, at the treacherous snow-covered pools and puddles which sent up formidable splashings of mud under the stamp of Dobbin's foot. A painter would, perhaps, have preferred 15 her in those moments when she was free from self-consciousness; but certainly the bloom on her cheeks was at its highest point of contrast with the surrounding drab when she arrived at the door of the Red House and saw Mr. Godfrey Cass ready to lift her from the pillion. She 20 wished her sister Priscilla had come up at the same time behind the servant, for then she would have contrived that Mr. Godfrey should have lifted off Priscilla first, and, in the meantime, she would have persuaded her father to go round to the horse block instead of alighting at the door- 25 steps. It was very painful, when you had made it quite clear to a young man that you were determined not to marry him, however much he might wish it, that he would still continue to pay you marked attentions; besides, why didn't he always show the same attentions, if he meant 30

them sincerely, instead of being so strange as Mr. Godfrey
Cass was, sometimes behaving as if he did n't want to speak
to her and taking no notice of her for weeks and weeks,
and then, all on a sudden, almost making love again?
5 Moreover, it was quite plain he had no real love for her,
else he would not let people have *that* to say of him
which they did say.   Did he suppose that Miss Nancy
Lammeter was to be won by any man, squire or no squire,
who led a bad life?   That was not what she had been used
10 to see in her own father, who was the soberest and best
man in that countryside, only a little hot and hasty now
and then, if things were not done to the minute.

   All these thoughts rushed through Miss Nancy's mind,
in their habitual succession, in the moments between her
15 first sight of Mr. Godfrey Cass standing at the door and
her own arrival there.   Happily, the Squire came out, too,
and gave a loud greeting to her father, so that, somehow,
under cover of this noise she seemed to find concealment
for her confusion and neglect of any suitably formal be-
20 havior while she was being lifted from the pillion by
strong arms which seemed to find her ridiculously small
and light.   And there was the best reason for hastening
into the house at once, since the snow was beginning to fall
again, threatening an unpleasant journey for such guests as
25 were still on the road.   These were a small minority; for
already the afternoon was beginning to decline, and there
would, not be too much time for the ladies who came from
a distance to attire themselves in readiness for the early tea
which was to inspirit them for the dance.

30   There was a buzz of voices through the house as Miss
Nancy entered, mingled with the scrape of a fiddle pre-
luding in the kitchen; but the Lammeters were guests
whose arrival had evidently been thought of so much that
it had been watched for from the windows, for Mrs. Kimble,

who did the honors at the Red House on these great
occasions, came forward to meet Miss Nancy in the hall
and conduct her upstairs. Mrs. Kimble was the Squire's
sister, as well as the doctor's wife, — a double dignity,
with which her diameter was in direct proportion; so that, 5
a journey upstairs being rather fatiguing to her, she did
not oppose Miss Nancy's request to be allowed to find her
way alone to the blue room, where the Miss Lammeters'
bandboxes had been deposited on their arrival in the
morning. 10

There was hardly a bedroom in the house where feminine
compliments were not passing and feminine toilettes going
forward in various stages, in space made scanty by extra
beds spread upon the floor; and Miss Nancy, as she
entered the blue room, had to make her little formal 15
curtsy to a group of six. On the one hand, there were
ladies no less important than the two Miss Gunns, the
wine merchant's daughters from Lytherly, dressed in the
height of fashion, with the tightest skirts and the shortest
waists, and gazed at by Miss Ladbrook (of the Old 20
Pastures) with a shyness not unsustained by inward
criticism. Partly, Miss Ladbrook felt that her own skirt
must be regarded as unduly lax by the Miss Gunns, and,
partly, that it was a pity the Miss Gunns did not show
that judgment which she herself would show if she were 25
in their place, by stopping a little on this side of the
fashion. On the other hand, Mrs. Ladbrook was standing
in skull-cap and front, with her turban in her hand,
curtsying and smiling blandly and saying, "After you,
ma'am," to another lady in similar circumstances, who 30
had politely offered the precedence at the looking-glass.

But Miss Nancy had no sooner made her curtsy than an
elderly lady came forward, whose full white muslin ker-
chief and mob-cap round her curls of smooth gray hair

were in daring contrast with the puffed yellow stains and top-knotted caps of her neighbors. She approached Miss Nancy with much primness, and said, with a slow, treble suavity :

5 " Niece, I hope I see you well in health." Miss Nancy kissed her aunt's cheek dutifully, and answered, with the same sort of amiable primness, " Quite well, I thank you, aunt; and I hope I see you the same."

" Thank you, niece ; I keep my health for the present.
10 And how is my brother-in-law ? "

These dutiful questions and answers were continued until it was ascertained in detail that the Lammeters were all as well as usual, and the Osgoods likewise ; also that niece Priscilla must certainly arrive shortly, and that
15 traveling on pillions in snowy weather was unpleasant, though a joseph was a great protection. Then Nancy was formally introduced to her aunt's visitors, the Miss Gunns, as being the daughters of a mother known to *their* mother, though now for the first time induced to make a
20 journey into these parts; and these ladies were so taken by surprise at finding such a lovely face and figure in an out-of-the-way country place that they began to feel some curiosity about the dress she would put on when she took off her joseph. Miss Nancy, whose thoughts were always
25 conducted with the propriety and moderation conspicuous in her manners, remarked to herself that the Miss Gunns were rather hard-featured than otherwise, and that such very low dresses as they wore might have been attributed to vanity if their shoulders had been pretty, but that, being
30 as they were, it was not reasonable to suppose that they showed their necks from a love of display, but rather from some obligation not inconsistent with sense and modesty. She felt convinced, as she opened her box, that this must be her Aunt Osgood's opinion, for Miss Nancy's mind

resembled her aunt's to a degree that everybody said was
surprising, considering the kinship was on Mr. Osgood's
side; and, though you might not have supposed it from
the formality of their greeting, there was a devoted
attachment and mutual admiration between aunt and 5
niece. Even Miss Nancy's refusal of her cousin Gilbert
Osgood (on the ground solely that he was her cousin),
though it had grieved her aunt greatly, had not in the
least cooled the preference which had determined her
to leave Nancy several of her hereditary ornaments, let 10
Gilbert's future wife be whom she might.

Three of the ladies quickly retired, but the Miss Gunns
were quite content that Mrs. Osgood's inclination to re-
main with her niece gave them also a reason for staying
to see the rustic beauty's toilette. And it was really a 15
pleasure, from the first opening of the bandbox, where
everything smelt of lavender and rose leaves, to the
clasping of the small coral necklace that fitted closely
round her little white neck. Everything belonging to
Miss Nancy was of delicate purity and nattiness; not a 20
crease was where it had no business to be, not a bit of
her linen professed whiteness without fulfilling its profession; the very pins on her pincushion were stuck in
after a pattern from which she was careful to allow no
aberration; and as for her own person, it gave the same 25
idea of perfect unvarying neatness as the body of a little
bird. It is true that her light-brown hair was cropped
behind like a boy's, and was dressed in front in a number
of flat rings that lay quite away from her face; but there
was no sort of coiffure that could make Miss Nancy's 30
cheek and neck look otherwise than pretty; and when
at last she stood complete in her silvery twilled silk, her
lace tucker, her coral necklace, and coral eardrops, the
Miss Gunns could see nothing to criticise except her

hands, which bore the traces of butter making, cheese crushing, and even still coarser work. But Miss Nancy was not ashamed of that, for while she was dressing she narrated to her aunt how she and Priscilla had packed
5 their boxes yesterday because this morning was baking morning, and since they were leaving home, it was desirable to make a good supply of meat pies for the kitchen ; and as she concluded this judicious remark she turned to the Miss Gunns that she might not commit the
10 rudeness of not including them in the conversation. The Miss Gunns smiled stiffly, and thought what a pity it was that these rich country people, who could afford to buy such good clothes (really Miss Nancy's lace and silk were very costly), should be brought up in utter ignorance
15 and vulgarity. She actually said "mate" for "meat," "'appen" for "perhaps," and "oss" for "horse," which to young ladies living in good Lytherly society, who habitually said 'orse, even in domestic privacy, and only said 'appen on the right occasions, was necessarily shock-
20 ing. Miss Nancy, indeed, had never been to any school higher than Dame Tedman's ; her acquaintance with profane literature hardly went beyond the rhymes she had worked in her large sampler under the lamb and the shepherdess ; and in order to balance an account,
25 she was obliged to effect her subtraction by removing visible metallic shillings and sixpences from a visible metallic total. There is hardly a servant maid in these days who is not better informed than Miss Nancy ; yet she had the essential attributes of a lady, — high verac-
30 ity, delicate honor in her dealings, deference to others, and refined personal habits ; and, lest these should not suffice to convince grammatical fair ones that her feel-ings can at all resemble theirs, I will add that she was slightly proud and exacting, and as constant in her affec-

tion towards a baseless opinion as towards an erring
lover.

The anxiety about sister Priscilla, which had grown
rather active by the time the coral necklace was clasped,
was happily ended by the entrance of that cheerful-
looking lady herself, with a face made blowzy by cold
and damp. After the first questions and greetings, she
turned to Nancy and surveyed her from head to foot,
then wheeled her round to ascertain that the back view
was equally faultless.

"What do you think o' *these* gowns, Aunt Osgood?"
said Priscilla, while Nancy helped her to unrobe.

"Very handsome, indeed, niece," said Mrs. Osgood,
with a slight increase of formality. She always thought
niece Priscilla too rough.

"I'm obliged to have the same as Nancy, you know,
for all I'm five years older and it makes me look yellow;
for she never *will* have anything without I have mine
just like it, because she wants us to look like sisters.
And I tell her folks 'ull think it's my weakness makes
me fancy as I shall look pretty in what she looks pretty
in. For I *am* ugly — there's no denying that; I feature
my father's family. But, law! I don't mind, do you?"
Priscilla here turned to the Miss Gunns, rattling on in
too much preoccupation with the delight of talking to
notice that her candor was not appreciated. "The pretty
uns do for fly-catchers — they keep the men off us. I've
no opinion o' the men, Miss Gunn — I don't know what
you have. And as for fretting and stewing about what
they'll think of you from morning till night, and making
your life uneasy about what they're doing when they're
out o' your sight, as I tell Nancy, it's a folly no woman
need be guilty of, if she's got a good father and a good
home; let her leave it to them as have got no fortin, and

can't help themselves. As I say, Mr. Have-your-own-way is the best husband and the only one I'd ever promise to obey. I know it is n't pleasant, when you 've been used to living in a big way and managing hogsheads
5 and all that, to go and put your nose in by somebody else's fireside or to sit down by yourself to a scrag or a knuckle; but, thank God! my father's a sober man and likely to live, and if you 've got a man by the chimney corner, it does n't matter if he 's childish — the business
10 need n't be broke up."

The delicate process of getting her narrow gown over her head without injury to her smooth curls obliged Miss Priscilla to pause in this rapid survey of life, and Mrs. Osgood seized the opportunity of rising and saying:
15 "Well, niece, you 'll follow us. The Miss Gunns will like to go down."

"Sister," said Nancy, when they were alone, "you 've offended the Miss Gunns, I 'm sure."

"What have I done, child?" said Priscilla, in some
20 alarm.

"Why, you asked them if they minded about being ugly — you 're so very blunt."

"Law, did I? Well, it popped out; it 's a mercy I said no more, for I 'm a bad un to live with folks when
25 they don't like the truth. But, as for being ugly, look at me, child, in this silver-colored silk — I told you how it 'ud be — I look as yellow as a daffadil. Anybody 'ud say you wanted to make a malkin of me."

"No, Priscy, don't say so. I begged and prayed of
30 you not to let us have this silk if you 'd like another better. I was willing to have *your* choice, you know I was," said Nancy, in anxious self-vindication.

"Nonsense, child! you know you 'd set your heart on this; and reason good, for you 're the color o' cream. It 'ud be fine doings for you to dress yourself to suit *my* skin. What I find fault with is that notion o' yours as I must dress myself just like you. But you do as you like with me — you always did, from when first you begun to walk. If you wanted to go the field's length you'd go; and there was no whipping you, for you looked as prim and innicent as a daisy all the while."

"Priscy," said Nancy gently, as she fastened a coral necklace exactly like her own round Priscilla's neck, which was very far from being like her own, "I'm sure I'm willing to give way as far as is right, but who shouldn't dress alike if it isn't sisters? Would you have us go about looking as if we were no kin to one another — us that have got no mother and not another sister in the world? I'd do what was right, if I dressed in a gown dyed with cheese-coloring; and I'd rather you'd choose, and let me wear what pleases you."

"There you go again! You'd come round to the same thing if one talked to you from Saturday night till Saturday morning. It'll be fine fun to see how you'll master your husband and never raise your voice above the singing o' the kettle all the while. I like to see the men mastered!"

"Don't talk *so*, Priscy," said Nancy, blushing. "You know I don't mean ever to be married."

"Oh, you never mean a fiddlestick's end!" said Priscilla, as she arranged her discarded dress and closed her bandbox. "Who shall *I* have to work for when father's gone if you are to go and take notions in your head and be an old maid, because some folks are no better than they should be? I haven't a bit o' patience with you — sitting on an addled egg forever, as if there was never a fresh un in the world. One old maid's enough out o' two sisters; and I shall do credit to a single life, for God

A'mighty meant me for it. Come, we can go down now. I 'm as ready as a malkin *can* be ; there 's nothing a-wanting to frighten the crows, now I 've got my eardroppers in."

5　As the two Miss Lammeters walked into the large parlor together, any one who did not know the character of both might certainly have supposed that the reason why the square-shouldered, clumsy, high-featured Priscilla wore a dress the facsimile of her pretty sister's was either 10 the mistaken vanity of the one or the malicious contrivance of the other in order to set off her own rare beauty. But the good-natured, self-forgetful cheeriness and common sense of Priscilla would soon have dissipated the one suspicion, and the modest calm of Nancy's speech 15 and manners told clearly of a mind free from all disavowed devices.

Places of honor had been kept for the Miss Lammeters near the head of the principal tea table in the wainscoted parlor, now looking fresh and pleasant with handsome 20 branches of holly, yew, and laurel from the abundant growths of the old garden ; and Nancy felt an inward flutter, that no firmness of purpose could prevent, when she saw Mr. Godfrey Cass advancing to lead her to a seat between himself and Mr. Crackenthorp, while Priscilla 25 was called to the opposite side between her father and the Squire. It certainly did make some difference to Nancy that the lover she had given up was the young man of quite the highest consequence in the parish,— at home in a venerable and unique parlor, which was the extremity 30 of grandeur in her experience, a parlor where *she* might one day have been mistress, with the consciousness that she was spoken of as " Madam Cass," the Squire's wife. These circumstances exalted her inward drama in her own eyes, and deepened the emphasis with which she declared

to herself that not the most dazzling rank should induce
her to marry a man whose conduct showed him careless
of his character, but that " love once, love always " was
the motto of a true and pure woman, and no man should
ever have any right over her which would be a call on her   5
to destroy the dried flowers that she treasured, and always
would treasure, for Godfrey Cass's sake. And Nancy
was capable of keeping her word to herself under very
trying conditions. Nothing but a becoming blush be-
trayed the moving thoughts that urged themselves upon   10
her as she accepted the seat next to Mr. Crackenthorp ;
for she was so instinctively neat and adroit in all her
actions and her pretty lips met each other with such quiet
firmness that it would have been difficult for her to appear
agitated.   15

It was not the rector's practice to let a charming blush
pass without an appropriate compliment. He was not in
the least lofty or aristocratic, but simply a merry-eyed,
small-featured, gray-haired man, with his chin propped by
an ample many-creased white neckcloth which seemed to   20
predominate over every other point in his person, and
somehow to impress its peculiar character on his remarks ;
so that to have considered his amenities apart from his
cravat would have been a severe, and perhaps a dangerous,
effort of abstraction.   25

" Ha, Miss Nancy," he said, turning his head within
his cravat and smiling down pleasantly upon her, " when
anybody pretends this has been a severe winter I shall tell
them I saw the roses blooming on New Year's Eve — eh,
Godfrey, what do *you* say ? "   30

Godfrey made no reply, and avoided looking at Nancy
very markedly ; for, though these complimentary personalities were held to be in excellent taste in old-fashioned
Raveloe society, reverent love has a politeness of its own

which it teaches to men otherwise of small schooling. But the Squire was rather impatient at Godfrey's showing himself a dull spark in this way. By this advanced hour of the day the Squire was always in higher spirits than we have seen him in at the breakfast table, and felt it quite pleasant to fulfill the hereditary duty of being noisily jovial and patronizing; the large silver snuffbox was in active service and was offered without fail to all neighbors from time to time, however often they might have declined the favor. At present, the Squire had only given an express welcome to the heads of families as they appeared; but always as the evening deepened his hospitality rayed out more widely, till he had tapped the youngest guests on the back and shown a peculiar fondness for their presence, in the full belief that they must feel their lives made happy by their belonging to a parish where there was such a hearty man as Squire Cass to invite them and wish them well. Even in this early stage of the jovial mood, it was natural that he should wish to supply his son's deficiencies by looking and speaking for him.

"Ay, ay," he began, offering his snuffbox to Mr. Lammeter, who for the second time bowed his head and waved his hand in stiff rejection of the offer, "us old fellows may wish ourselves young to-night when we see the mistletoe bough in the white parlor. It's true, most things are gone back'ard in these last thirty years — the country's going down since the old king fell ill. But when I look at Miss Nancy here I begin to think the lasses keep up their quality; ding me if I remember a sample to match her, not when I was a fine young fellow, and thought a deal about my pigtail. No offense to you, madam," he added, bending to Mrs. Crackenthorp, who sat by him, "I did n't know *you* when you were as young as Miss Nancy here."

Mrs. Crackenthorp — a small, blinking woman, who fidgeted incessantly with her lace, ribbons, and gold chain, turning her head about and making subdued noises, very much like a guinea pig that twitches its nose and soliloquizes in all company indiscriminately — now blinked and fidgeted towards the Squire, and said, "Oh, no — no offense."

This emphatic compliment of the Squire's to Nancy was felt by others besides Godfrey to have a diplomatic significance; and her father gave a slight additional erectness to his back as he looked across the table at her with complacent gravity. That grave and orderly senior was not going to bate a jot of his dignity by seeming elated at the notion of a match between his family and the Squire's; he was gratified by any honor paid to his daughter, but he must see an alteration in several ways before his consent would be vouchsafed. His spare but healthy person and high-featured, firm face, that looked as if it had never been flushed by excess, was in strong contrast, not only with the Squire's, but with the appearance of the Raveloe farmers generally, in accordance with a favorite saying of his own, that "breed was stronger than pasture."

"Miss Nancy's wonderful like what her mother was, though; is n't she, Kimble?" said the stout lady of that name, looking round for her husband.

But Doctor Kimble (county apothecaries in old days enjoyed that title without authority of diploma), being a thin and agile man, was flitting about the room with his hands in his pockets, making himself agreeable to his feminine patients, with medical impartiality, and being welcomed everywhere as a doctor by hereditary right — not one of those miserable apothecaries who canvass for practice in strange neighborhoods and spend all their

income in starving their one horse, but a man of substance, able to keep an extravagant table like the best of his patients. Time out of mind the Raveloe doctor had been a Kimble; Kimble was inherently a doctor's name, and
5 it was difficult to contemplate firmly the melancholy fact that the actual Kimble had no son, so that his practice might one day be handed over to a successor with the incongruous name of Taylor or Johnson. But in that case the wiser people in Raveloe would employ Dr. Blick, of
10 Flitton — as less unnatural.

"Did you speak to me, my dear?" said the authentic doctor, coming quickly to his wife's side; but, as if foreseeing that she would be too much out of breath to repeat her remark, he went on immediately, "Ha, Miss Priscilla,
15 the sight of you revives the taste of that super-excellent pork pie. I hope the batch is n't near an end."

"Yes, indeed, it is, doctor," said Priscilla; "but I 'll answer for it the next shall be as good. My pork pies don't turn out well by chance."

20 "Not as your doctoring does, eh, Kimble? — because folks forget to take your physic, eh?" said the Squire, who regarded physic and doctors as many loyal churchmen regard the church and the clergy, — tasting a joke against them when he was in health, but impatiently eager
25 for their aid when anything was the matter with him. He tapped his box and looked round with a triumphant laugh.

"Ah, she has a quick wit, my friend Priscilla has," said the doctor, choosing to attribute the epigram to a
30 lady rather than allow a brother-in-law that advantage over him. "She saves a little pepper to sprinkle over her talk; that 's the reason why she never puts too much into her pies. There 's my wife, now, she never has an answer at her tongue's end; but if I offend her, she 's

sure to scarify my throat with black pepper the next day or else give me the colic with watery greens. That's an awful tit for tat." Here the vivacious doctor made a pathetic grimace.

"Did you ever hear the like?" said Mrs. Kimble, laughing above her double chin with much good humor, aside to Mrs. Crackenthorp, who blinked and nodded, and amiably intended to smile; but the intention lost itself in small twitchings and noises.

"I suppose that's the sort of tit for tat adopted in your profession, Kimble, if you've a grudge against a patient," said the rector.

"Never do have a grudge against our patients," said Mr. Kimble, "except when they leave us; and then, you see, we have n't the chance of prescribing for 'em. Ha, Miss Nancy," he continued, suddenly skipping to Nancy's side, "you won't forget your promise? You're to save a dance for me, you know."

"Come, come, Kimble, don't you be too for'ard," said the Squire. "Give the young uns fair play. There's my son Godfrey 'll be wanting to have a round with you if you run off with Miss Nancy. He's bespoke her for the first dance, I'll be bound. Eh, sir, what do you say?" he continued, throwing himself backward, and looking at Godfrey. "Have n't you asked Miss Nancy to open the dance with you?"

Godfrey, sorely uncomfortable under this significant insistance about Nancy, and afraid to think where it would end by the time his father had set his usual hospitable example of drinking before and after supper, saw no course open but to turn to Nancy and say, with as little awkwardness as possible:

"No; I've not asked her yet, but I hope she'll consent — if somebody else has n't been before me."

"No, I've not engaged myself," said Nancy quietly, though blushingly. (If Mr. Godfrey founded any hopes on her consenting to dance with him, he would soon be undeceived; but there was no need for her to be uncivil.)

5　"Then I hope you've no objections to dancing with me," said Godfrey, beginning to lose the sense that there was anything uncomfortable in this arrangement.

"No, no objections," said Nancy, in a cold tone.

"Ah, well, you're a lucky fellow, Godfrey," said Uncle 10 Kimble; "but you're my godson, so I won't stand in your way. Else I'm not so very old, eh, my dear?" he went on, skipping to his wife's side again. "You wouldn't mind my having a second after you were gone — not if I cried a good deal first?"

15　"Come, come, take a cup o' tea and stop your tongue, do," said good-humored Mrs. Kimble, feeling some pride in a husband who must be regarded as so clever and amusing by the company generally. If he had only not been irritable at cards!

20　While safe, well-tested personalities were enlivening the tea in this way, the sound of the fiddle approaching within a distance at which it could be heard distinctly made the young people look at each other with sympathetic impatience for the end of the meal.

25　"Why, there's Solomon in the hall," said the Squire, "and playing my favo'rite tune, *I* believe, — 'The Flaxen-headed Plowboy,' — he's for giving us a hint as we aren't enough in a hurry to hear him play. Bob," he called out to his third, long-legged son, who was at the other end of 30 the room, "open the door, and tell Solomon to come in. He shall give us a tune here."

Bob obeyed, and Solomon walked in, fiddling as he walked, for he would on no account break off in the middle of a tune.

"Here, Solomon," said the Squire, with loud patronage. "Round here, my man. Ah, I knew it was 'The Flaxenheaded Plowboy'; there 's no finer tune."

Solomon Macey, a small, hale old man, with an abundant crop of long white hair reaching nearly to his shoulders, advanced to the indicated spot, bowing reverently while he fiddled, as much as to say that he respected the company though he respected the keynote more. As soon as he had repeated the tune and lowered his fiddle, he bowed again to the Squire and the rector, and said, "I hope I see your honor and your reverence well, and wishing you health and long life and a happy New Year. And wishing the same to you, Mr. Lammeter, sir; and to the other gentlemen and the madams and the young lasses."

As Solomon uttered the last words, he bowed in all directions solicitously, lest he should be wanting in due respect. But thereupon he immediately began to prelude, and fell into the tune which he knew would be taken as a special compliment by Mr. Lammeter.

"Thank ye, Solomon, thank ye," said Mr. Lammeter when the fiddle paused again. "That 's 'Over the Hills and Far Away,' that is. My father used to say to me, whenever we heard that tune, 'Ah, lad, *I* come from over the hills and far away.' There 's a many tunes I don't make head or tail of; but that speaks to me like the blackbird's whistle. I suppose it 's the name; there 's a deal in the name of a tune."

But Solomon was already impatient to prelude again, and presently broke with much spirit into "Sir Roger de Coverley," at which there was a sound of chairs pushed back and laughing voices.

"Ay, ay, Solomon, we know what that means," said the Squire, rising. "It 's time to begin the dance, eh? Lead the way, then, and we 'll all follow you."

So Solomon, holding his white head on one side and
playing vigorously, marched forward at the head of the
gay procession into the white parlor, where the mistletoe
bough was hung, and multitudinous tallow candles made
5 rather a brilliant effect, gleaming from among the berried
holly boughs, and reflected in the old-fashioned oval
mirrors fastened in the panels of the white wainscot.   A
quaint procession !   Old Solomon, in his seedy clothes
and long white locks, seemed to be luring that decent
10 company by the magic scream of his fiddle — luring
discreet matrons in turban-shaped caps, nay, Mrs.
Crackenthorp herself, the summit of whose perpendicular
feather was on a level with the Squire's shoulder — luring
fair lasses complacently conscious of very short waists
15 and skirts blameless of frontfolds — luring burly fathers
in large variegated waistcoats, and ruddy sons, for the
most part shy and sheepish, in short nether garments and
very long coat tails.

Already Mr. Macey and a few other privileged villagers,
20 who were allowed to be spectators on these great occasions, were seated on benches placed for them near the
door ; and great was the admiration and satisfaction in
that quarter when the couples had formed themselves for
the dance, and the Squire led off with Mrs. Crackenthorp,
25 joining hands with the rector and Mrs. Osgood.   That
was as it should be — that was what everybody had been
used to — and the charter of Raveloe seemed to be re-
newed by the ceremony.   It was not thought of as an un-
becoming levity for the old and middle-aged people to
30 dance a little before sitting down to cards, but, rather, as
part of their social duties.   For what were these if not
to be merry at appropriate times, interchanging visits
and poultry with due frequency, paying each other old-
established compliments in sound, traditional phrases,

passing well-tried personal jokes, urging your guests to eat and drink too much out of hospitality, and eating and drinking too much in your neighbor's house to show that you liked your cheer? And the parson naturally set an example in these social duties. For it would not have been possible for the Raveloe mind, without a peculiar revelation, to know that a clergyman should be a pale-faced memento of solemnities, instead of a reasonably faulty man whose exclusive authority to read prayers and preach, to christen, marry, and bury you, necessarily coexisted with the right to sell you the ground to be buried in and to take tithe in kind; on which last point, of course, there was a little grumbling, but not to the extent of irreligion — not of deeper significance than the grumbling at the rain, which was by no means accompanied with a spirit of impious defiance, but with a desire that the prayer for fine weather might be read forthwith.

There was no reason, then, why the rector's dancing should not be received as part of the fitness of things quite as much as the Squire's, or why, on the other hand, Mr. Macey's official respect should restrain him from subjecting the parson's performance to that criticism with which minds of extraordinary acuteness must necessarily contemplate the doings of their fallible fellow-men.

"The Squire's pretty springe, considering his weight," said Mr. Macey, "and he stamps uncommon well. But Mr. Lammeter beats 'em all for shapes; you see, he holds his head like a sodger, and he isn't so cushiony as most o' the oldish gentlefolks — they run fat in general — and he's got a fine leg. The parson's nimble enough, but he hasn't got much of a leg; it's a bit too thick down'ard, and his knees might be a bit nearer wi'out damage — but he might do worse, he might do worse.

Though he has n't that grand way o' waving his hand as the Squire has."

"Talk o' nimbleness, look at Mrs. Osgood," said Ben Winthrop, who was holding his son Aaron between his knees. "She trips along with her little steps, so as nobody can see how she goes; it's like as if she had little wheels to her feet. She does n't look a day older nor last year; she's the finest-made woman as is, let the next be where she will."

"I don't heed how the women are made," said Mr. Macey, with some contempt. "They wear nayther coat nor breeches; you can't make much out o' their shapes."

"Fayder," said Aaron, whose feet were busy beating out the tune, "how does that big cock's feather stick in Mrs. Crackenthorp's yead? Is there a little hole for it, like in my shuttle-cock?"

"Hush, lad, hush; that's the way the ladies dress theirselves, that is," said the father, adding, however, in an undertone to Mr. Macey, "It does make her look funny, though — partly like a short-necked bottle wi' a long quill in it. Hey, by jingo, there's the young Squire leading off now, wi' Miss Nancy for partners! There's a lass for you! — like a pink and white posy — there's nobody 'ud think as anybody could be so pritty. I should n't wonder if she's Madam Cass some day, arter all — and nobody more rightfuller, for they'd make a fine match. You can find nothing against Master Godfrey's shapes, Macey, *I*'ll bet a penny."

Mr. Macey screwed up his mouth, leaned his head further on one side, and twirled his thumbs with a presto movement as his eyes followed Godfrey up the dance. At last he summed up his opinion.

"Pretty well down'ard, but a bit too round i' the shoulder blades. And as for them coats as he gets from the

Flitton tailor, they're a poor cut to pay double money for."

"Ah, Mr. Macey, you and me are two folks," said Ben, slightly indignant at this carping. "When I've got a pot o' good ale, I like to swaller it and do my inside good, i'stead o' smelling and staring at it to see if I can't find faut wi' the brewing. I should like you to pick me out a finer limbed young fellow nor Master Godfrey — one as 'ud knock you down easier, or 's more pleasanter looksed when he's piert and merry."

"Tchuh!" said Mr. Macey, provoked to increased severity, "he isn't come to his right color yet; he's partly like a slack-baked pie. And I doubt he's got a soft place in his head, else why should he be turned round the finger by that offal Dunsey as nobody's seen o' late, and let him kill that fine hunting hoss as was the talk o' the country? And one while he was allays after Miss Nancy, and then it all went off again, like a smell o' hot porridge, as I may say. That wasn't my way when *I* went a-coorting."

"Ah, but mayhap Miss Nancy hung off like, and your lass didn't," said Ben.

"I should say she didn't," said Mr. Macey significantly. "Before I said 'sniff' I took care to know as she'd say 'snaff,' and pretty quick, too. I wasn't a-going to open *my* mouth, like a dog at a fly, and snap it to again, wi' nothing to swaller."

"Well, I think Miss Nancy's a-coming round again," said Ben, "for Master Godfrey doesn't look so downhearted to-night. And I see he's for taking her away to sit down, now they're at the end o' the dance; that looks like sweethearting, that does."

The reason why Godfrey and Nancy had left the dance was not so tender as Ben imagined. In the close press

of couples a slight accident had happened to Nancy's
dress, which, while it was short enough to show her neat
ankle in front, was long enough behind to be caught
under the stately stamp of the Squire's foot, so as to rend
5 certain stitches at the waist, and cause much sisterly
agitation in Priscilla's mind, as well as serious concern
in Nancy's. One's thoughts may be much occupied with
love struggles, but hardly so as to be insensible to a
disorder in the general framework of things. Nancy had
10 no sooner completed her duty in the figure they were
dancing than she said to Godfrey, with a deep blush,
that she must go and sit down till Priscilla could come
to her; for the sisters had already exchanged a short
whisper and an open-eyed glance full of meaning. No
15 reason less urgent than this could have prevailed on
Nancy to give Godfrey this opportunity of sitting apart
with her. As for Godfrey, he was feeling so happy and
oblivious under the long charm of the country dance
with Nancy that he got rather bold on the strength of her
20 confusion, and was capable of leading her straight away,
without leave asked, into the adjoining small parlor,
where the card tables were set.

"Oh, no, thank you," said Nancy coldly, as soon as she
perceived where he was going, "not in there. I'll wait
25 here till Priscilla's ready to come to me. I'm sorry to
bring you out of the dance and make myself troublesome."

"Why, you'll be more comfortable here by yourself,"
said the artful Godfrey; "I'll leave you here till your
sister can come." He spoke in an indifferent tone.

30 That was an agreeable proposition, and just what Nancy
desired; why, then, was she a little hurt that Mr. Godfrey should make it? They entered, and she seated herself on a chair against one of the card tables, as the stiffest
and most unapproachable position she could choose.

"Thank you, sir," she said immediately. "I need n't give you any more trouble. I 'm sorry you 've had such an unlucky partner."

"That 's very ill-natured of you," said Godfrey, standing by her without any sign of intended departure, "to be sorry you 've danced with me."

"Oh, no, sir, I don't mean to say what 's ill-natured at all," said Nancy, looking distractingly prim and pretty. "When gentlemen have so many pleasures, one dance can matter but very little."

"You know that is n't true. You know one dance with you matters more to me than all the other pleasures in the world."

It was a long, long while since Godfrey had said anything so direct as that, and Nancy was startled. But her instinctive dignity and repugnance to any show of emotion made her sit perfectly still, and only throw a little more decision into her voice, as she said :

"No, indeed, Mr. Godfrey, that 's not known to me, and I have very good reasons for thinking different. But if it 's true, I don't wish to hear it."

"Would you never forgive me, then, Nancy — never think well of me, let what would happen — would you never think the present made amends for the past? Not if I turned a good fellow, and gave up everything you did n't like ? "

Godfrey was half conscious that this sudden opportunity of speaking to Nancy alone had driven him beside himself ; but blind feeling had got the mastery of his tongue. Nancy really felt much agitated by the possibility Godfrey's words suggested, but this very pressure of emotion that she was in danger of finding too strong for her roused all her power of self-command.

"I should be glad to see a good change in anybody,

Mr. Godfrey," she answered, with the slightest discernible difference of tone, " but it 'ud be better if no change was wanted."

" You 're very hard-hearted, Nancy," said Godfrey pet-
5 tishly. " You might encourage me to be a better fellow. I 'm very miserable — but you 've no feeling."

" I think those have the least feeling that act wrong to begin with," said Nancy, sending out a flash in spite of herself. Godfrey was delighted with that little flash, and
10 would have liked to go on and make her quarrel with him ; Nancy was so exasperatingly quiet and firm. But she was not indifferent to him *yet*.

The entrance of Priscilla, bustling forward and saying, " Dear heart alive, child, let us look at this gown," cut
15 off Godfrey's hopes of a quarrel.

" I suppose I must go now," he said to Priscilla.

" It 's no matter to me whether you go or stay," said that frank lady, searching for something in her pocket, with a preoccupied brow.

20 " Do *you* want me to go ? " said Godfrey, looking at Nancy, who was now standing up by Priscilla's order.

" As you like," said Nancy, trying to recover all her former coldness and looking down carefully at the hem of her gown.

25 " Then I like to stay," said Godfrey, with a reckless determination to get as much of this joy as he could to-night and think nothing of the morrow.

CHAPTER XII.

WHILE Godfrey Cass was taking draughts of forgetfulness from the sweet presence of Nancy, willingly losing all sense of that hidden bond which at other moments galled and fretted him so as to mingle irritation with the very sunshine, Godfrey's wife was walking with slow, uncertain steps through the snow-covered Raveloe lanes, carrying her child in her arms.

This journey on New Year's Eve was a premeditated act of vengeance which she had kept in her heart ever since Godfrey, in a fit of passion, had told her he would sooner die than acknowledge her as his wife. There would be a great party at the Red House on New Year's Eve, she knew; her husband would be smiling and smiled upon, hiding *her* existence in the darkest corner of his heart. But she would mar his pleasure; she would go in her dingy rags, with her faded face, once as handsome as the best, with her little child that had its father's hair and eyes, and disclose herself to the Squire as his eldest son's wife. It is seldom that the miserable can help regarding their misery as a wrong inflicted by those who are less miserable. Molly knew that the cause of her dingy rags was not her husband's neglect, but the demon opium to whom she was enslaved, body and soul, except in the lingering mother's tenderness that refused to give him her hungry child. She knew this well; and yet, in the moments of wretched, unbenumbed consciousness, the sense of her want and degradation transformed itself continually into bitterness towards Godfrey. *He* was well off; and if she had her rights she would be well off, too. The belief that he repented his marriage and suffered from it only aggravated her vindictiveness. Just and self-reproving thoughts do not come to us too thickly, even in the purest air and with the best lessons of heaven and earth ; how should those white-winged, delicate messengers make their way to Molly's poisoned chamber, inhabited by no higher memories than those of a barmaid's paradise of pink ribbons and gentlemen's jokes ?

She had set out at an early hour, but had lingered on the road, inclined by her indolence to believe that if she waited under a warm shed the snow would cease to fall. She had waited longer than she knew, and now that she found herself belated in the snow-hidden ruggedness of the long lanes, even the animation of a vindictive purpose could not keep her spirit from failing. It was seven o'clock, and by this time she was not very far from Raveloe, but she was not familiar enough with those monotonous lanes to know how near she was to her journey's end. She needed comfort, and she knew but one comforter, — the familiar demon in her bosom ; but she hesitated a moment, after drawing out the black remnant, before she raised it to her lips. In that moment the mother's love pleaded for painful consciousness rather than oblivion — pleaded to be left in aching weariness rather than to have the encircling arms benumbed so that they could not feel the dear burden. In another moment Molly had flung something away, but it was not the black remnant ; it was an empty phial. And she walked on again under the breaking cloud, from which there came now and then the light of a quickly veiled star, for a freezing wind had sprung up since the snowing had ceased. But she walked always more and more drowsily, and clutched more and more automatically the sleeping child at her bosom.

Slowly the demon was working his will, and cold and weariness were his helpers. Soon she felt nothing but a

supreme immediate longing that curtained off all futurity,
— the longing to lie down and sleep.   She had arrived at
a spot where her footsteps were no longer checked by a
hedgerow, and she had wandered vaguely, unable to distinguish any objects, notwithstanding the wide whiteness 5
around her and the growing starlight.   She sank down
against a straggling furze bush, an easy pillow enough ;
and the bed of snow, too, was soft.   She did not feel that
the bed was cold, and did not heed whether the child
would wake and cry for her.   But her arms had not yet 10
relaxed their instinctive clutch ; and the little one slum-
bered on as gently as if it had been rocked in a lace-
trimmed cradle.

But the complete torpor came at last ; the fingers lost
their tension, the arms unbent ; then the little head fell 15
away from the bosom, and the blue eyes opened wide on
the cold starlight.   At first there was a little peevish cry
of " mammy " and an effort to regain the pillowing arm
and bosom ; but mammy's ear was deaf, and the pillow
seemed to be slipping away backward.   Suddenly, as the 20
child rolled downward on its mother's knees, all wet with
snow, its eyes were caught by a bright, glancing light on
the white ground, and, with the ready transition of in-
fancy, it was immediately absorbed in watching the bright,
living thing running towards it, yet never arriving.   That 25
bright, living thing must be caught ; and in an instant the
child had slipped on all fours and held out one little hand
to catch the gleam.   But the gleam would not be caught
in that way, and now the head was held up to see where
the cunning gleam came from.   It came from a very 30
bright place ; and the little one, rising on its legs, toddled
through the snow, the old grimy shawl in which it was
wrapped trailing behind it, and the queer little bonnet
dangling at its back — toddled on to the open door of

Silas Marner's cottage, and right up to the warm hearth,
where there was a bright fire of logs and sticks, which
had thoroughly warmed the old sack (Silas's greatcoat)
spread out on the bricks to dry. The little one, accus-
5 tomed to be left to itself for long hours without notice
from its mother, squatted down on the sack and spread
its tiny hands towards the blaze, in perfect contentment,
gurgling and making many inarticulate communications
to the cheerful fire, like a new-hatched gosling beginning to
10 find itself comfortable. But presently the warmth had a
lulling effect, and the little golden head sank down on the
old sack, and the blue eyes were veiled by their delicate,
half-transparent lids.

But where was Silas Marner while this strange visitor
15 had come to his hearth? He was in the cottage, but he
did not see the child. During the last few weeks, since
he had lost his money, he had contracted the habit of
opening his door and looking out from time to time, as if
he thought that his money might be somehow coming
20 back to him, or that some trace, some news of it, might
be mysteriously on the road, and be caught by the listening
ear or the straining eye. It was chiefly at night, when he
was not occupied in his loom, that he fell into this repetition of an act for which he could have assigned no definite
25 purpose, and which can hardly be understood except by
those who have undergone a bewildering separation from
a supremely loved object. In the evening twilight, and
later whenever the night was not dark, Silas looked out
on that narrow prospect round the Stone-pits, listening
30 and gazing, not with hope, but with mere yearning and
unrest.

This morning he had been told by some of his neighbors that it was New Year's Eve, and that he must sit up
and hear the old year rung out and the new rung in,

because that was good luck and might bring his money
back again. This was only a friendly Raveloe way of
jesting with the half-crazy oddities of a miser, but it had
perhaps helped to throw Silas into a more than usually
excited state. Since the oncoming of twilight he had 5
opened his door again and again, though only to shut it
immediately at seeing all distance veiled by the falling
snow. But the last time he opened it the snow had ceased
and the clouds were parting here and there. He stood
and listened and gazed for a long while — there was really 10
something on the road coming towards him then, but he
caught no sign of it; and the stillness and the wide, track-
less snow seemed to narrow his solitude, and touched his
yearning with the chill of despair. He went in again, and
put his right hand on the latch of the door to close it; 15
but he did not close it. He was arrested, as he had been
already since his loss, by the invisible wand of catalepsy,
and stood like a graven image, with wide but sightless
eyes, holding open his door, powerless to resist either the
good or evil that might enter there. 20

When Marner's sensibility returned, he continued the
action which had been arrested and closed his door, unaware of the chasm in his consciousness, unaware of any
intermediate change, except that the light had grown dim
and that he was chilled and faint. He thought he had been 25
too long standing at the door and looking out. Turning
towards the hearth, where the two logs had fallen apart,
and sent forth only a red, uncertain glimmer, he seated
himself on his fireside chair, and was stopping to push his
logs together, when, to his blurred vision, it seemed as if 30
there were gold on the floor in front of the hearth. Gold!
— his own gold — brought back to him as mysteriously
as it had been taken away! He felt his heart begin to
beat violently, and for a few moments he was unable to

stretch out his hand and grasp the restored treasure. The heap of gold seemed to glow and get larger beneath his agitated gaze. He leaned forward at last and stretched forth his hand ; but, instead of the hard coin with the 5 familiar resisting outline, his fingers encountered soft, warm curls. In utter amazement, Silas fell on his knees and bent his head low to examine the marvel ; it was a sleeping child — a round, fair thing, with soft yellow rings all over its head. Could this be his little sister come back 10 to him in a dream, — his little sister whom he had carried about in his arms for a year before she died, when he was a small boy without shoes or stockings ? That was the first thought that darted across Silas's blank wonderment. *Was* it a dream ? He rose to his feet again, pushed his 15 logs together, and, throwing on some dried leaves and sticks, raised a flame ; but the flame did not disperse the vision — it only lit up more distinctly the little round form of the child and its shabby clothing. It was very much like his little sister. Silas sank into his chair, 20 powerless, under the double presence of an inexplicable surprise and a hurrying influx of memories. How and when had the child come in without his knowledge ? He had never been beyond the door. But along with that question, and almost thrusting it away, there was a vision 25 of the old home and the old streets leading to Lantern Yard, and within that vision another, of the thoughts which had been present with him in those far-off scenes. The thoughts were strange to him now, like old friend- ships impossible to revive ; and yet he had a dreamy 30 feeling that this child was somehow a message come to him from that far-off life. It stirred fibers that had never been moved in Raveloe — old quiverings of tenderness — old impressions of awe at the presentiment of some Power presiding over his life ; for his imagination had not yet extricated itself from the sense of mystery in the child's sudden presence, and had formed no conjectures of ordinary, natural means by which the event could have been brought about.

But there was a cry on the hearth; the child had awaked, and Marner stooped to lift it on his knee. It clung round his neck, and burst louder and louder into that mingling of inarticulate cries with "mammy" by which little children express the bewilderment of waking. Silas pressed it to him, and almost unconsciously uttered sounds of hushing tenderness, while he bethought himself that some of his porridge, which had got cool by the dying fire, would do to feed the child with if it were only warmed up a little.

He had plenty to do through the next hour. The porridge, sweetened with some dry brown sugar from an old store which he had refrained from using for himself, stopped the cries of the little one, and made her lift her blue eyes with a wide, quiet gaze at Silas, as he put the spoon into her mouth. Presently she slipped from his knee and began to toddle about, but with a pretty stagger that made Silas jump up and follow her lest she should fall against anything that would hurt her. But she only fell in a sitting posture on the ground, and began to pull at her boots, looking up at him with a crying face as if the boots hurt her. He took her on his knee again, but it was some time before it occurred to Silas's dull bachelor mind that the wet boots were the grievance, pressing on her warm ankles. He got them off with difficulty, and baby was at once happily occupied with the primary mystery of her own toes, inviting Silas, with much chuckling, to consider the mystery, too. But the wet boots had at last suggested to Silas that the child had been walking on the snow, and this roused him from his entire oblivion of any ordinary means by which it could have entered or been brought into his house. Under the prompting of this new idea, and without waiting to form conjectures, he raised the child in his arms and went to 5 the door. As soon as he had opened it there was the cry of "mammy" again, which Silas had not heard since the child's first hungry waking. Bending forward, he could just discern the marks made by the little feet on the virgin snow, and he followed their track to the furze 10 bushes. "Mammy!" the little one cried again and again, stretching itself forward so as almost to escape from Silas's arms, before he himself was aware that there was something more than the bush before him — that there was a human body, with the head sunk low in the furze, 15 and half covered with the shaken snow.

CHAPTER XIII.

It was after the early supper time at the Red House, and the entertainment was in that stage when bashfulness itself had passed into easy jollity, when gentlemen, conscious of unusual accomplishments, could at length be prevailed on to dance a hornpipe, and when the Squire preferred talking loudly, scattering snuff, and patting his visitors' backs to sitting longer at the whist table, — a choice exasperating to Uncle Kimble, who, being always volatile in sober business hours, became intense and bitter over cards and brandy, shuffled before his adversary's deal with a glare of suspicion, and turned up a mean trump card with an air of inexpressible disgust, as if in a world where such things could happen one might as well enter on a course of reckless profligacy. When the evening had advanced to this pitch of freedom and enjoyment, it was usual for the servants, the heavy duties of supper being well over, to get their share of amusement by coming to look on at the dancing; so that the back regions of the house were left in solitude.

There were two doors by which the white parlor was entered from the hall, and they were both standing open for the sake of air; but the lower one was crowded with the servants and villagers, and only the upper doorway was left free. Bob Cass was figuring in a hornpipe, and his father, very proud of this lithe son, whom he repeatedly declared to be just like himself in his young days in a tone that implied this to be the very highest stamp of juvenile merit, was the center of a group who had placed themselves opposite the performer, not far from the upper door. Godfrey was standing a little way off, not to admire his brother's dancing, but to keep sight of Nancy, who was seated in the group, near her father. He stood aloof, because he wished to avoid suggesting himself as a subject for the Squire's fatherly jokes in connection with matrimony and Miss Nancy Lammeter's beauty, which were likely to become more and more explicit. But he had the prospect of dancing with her again when the hornpipe was concluded, and in the meanwhile it was very pleasant to get long glances at her quite unobserved.

But when Godfrey was lifting his eyes from one of those long glances, they encountered an object as startling to him at that moment as if it had been an apparition from the dead. It *was* an apparition from that hidden life which lies, like a dark by-street, behind the goodly ornamented façade that meets the sunlight and the gaze of respectable admirers. It was his own child carried in Silas Marner's arms. That was his instantaneous impression, unaccompanied by doubt, though he had not seen the child for months past; and when the hope was rising that he might possibly be mistaken, Mr. Crackenthorp and Mr. Lammeter had already advanced to Silas, in astonishment at this strange advent. Godfrey joined them immediately, unable to rest without hearing every word, trying to control himself, but conscious that, if any one noticed him, they must see that he was white-lipped and trembling.

But now all eyes at that end of the room were bent on Silas Marner; the Squire himself had risen and asked angrily, " How's this? what's this? what do you do coming in here in this way?"

" I'm come for the doctor; I want the doctor," Silas had said, in the first moment, to Mr. Crackenthorp.

" Why, what's the matter, Marner?" said the rector.

"The doctor's here; but say quietly what you want him for."

"It's a woman," said Silas, speaking low and half-breathlessly, just as Godfrey came up. "She's dead, I think — dead in the snow at the Stone-pits — not far 5 from my door."

Godfrey felt a great throb; there was one terror in his mind at that moment: it was that the woman might *not* be dead. That was an evil terror, — an ugly inmate to have found a nestling-place in Godfrey's kindly disposi- 10 tion; but no disposition is a security from evil wishes to a man whose happiness hangs on duplicity.

"Hush, hush!" said Mr. Crackenthorp. "Go out into the hall there. I'll fetch the doctor to you. Found a woman in the snow — and think she's dead," he added, 15 speaking low, to the Squire. "Better say as little about it as possible; it will shock the ladies. Just tell them a poor woman is ill from cold and hunger. I'll go and fetch Kimble."

By this time, however, the ladies had pressed forward, 20 curious to know what could have brought the solitary linen weaver there under such strange circumstances, and interested in the pretty child, who, half alarmed and half attracted by the brightness and the numerous company, now frowned and hid her face, now lifted up her head 25 again and looked round placably, until a touch or a coax-ing word brought back the frown and made her bury her face with new determination.

"What child is it?" said several ladies at once, and, among the rest, Nancy Lammeter, addressing God- 30 frey.

"I don't know — some poor woman's who has been found in the snow, I believe," was the answer Godfrey wrung from himself with a terrible effort. ("After all, *am* I certain?" he hastened to add, in anticipation of his own conscience.)

"Why, you'd better leave the child here, then, Master Marner," said good-natured Mrs. Kimble, hesitating, how-
5 ever, to take those dingy clothes into contact with her own ornamented satin bodice.. "I'll tell one o' the girls to fetch it."

"No — no — I can't part with it, I can't let it go," said Silas abruptly. "It's come to me, I've a right to
10 keep it."

The proposition to take the child from him had come to Silas quite unexpectedly, and his speech, uttered under a strong sudden impulse, was almost like a revelation to himself; a minute before he had no distinct intention
15 about the child.

"Did you ever hear the like?" said Mrs. Kimble, in mild surprise, to her neighbor.

"Now, ladies, I must trouble you to stand aside," said Mr. Kimble, coming from the card room, in some bitter-
20 ness at the interruption, but drilled by the long habit of his profession into obedience to unpleasant calls, even when he was hardly sober.

"It's a nasty business turning out now, eh, Kimble?" said the Squire. "He might ha' gone for your young
25 fellow — the 'prentice, there — what's his name?"

"Might? ay, what's the use of talking about might?" growled Uncle Kimble, hastening out with Marner, and followed by Mr. Crackenthorp and Godfrey. "Get me a pair of thick boots, Godfrey, will you? And stay, let
30 somebody run to Winthrop's and fetch Dolly —she's the best woman to get. Ben was here himself before supper; is he gone?"

"Yes, sir, I met him," said Marner; "but I couldn't stop to tell him anything; only I said I was going for the doctor, and he said the doctor was at the Squire's. And I made haste and ran, and there was nobody to be seen at the back o' the house, and so I went in to where the company was."

The child, no longer distracted by the bright light and the smiling women's faces, began to cry and call for "mammy," though always clinging to Marner, who had apparently won her thorough confidence. Godfrey had come back with the boots, and felt the cry as if some fiber were drawn tight within him.

"I'll go," he said hastily, eager for some movement; "I'll go and fetch the woman — Mrs. Winthrop."

"Oh, pooh! send somebody else," said Uncle Kimble, hurrying away with Marner.

"You'll let me know if I can be of any use, Kimble," said Mr. Crackenthorp. But the doctor was out of hearing.

Godfrey, too, had disappeared; he was gone to snatch his hat and coat, having just reflection enough to remember that he must not look like a madman; but he rushed out of the house into the snow without heeding his thin shoes.

In a few minutes he was on his rapid way to the Stone-pits by the side of Dolly, who, though feeling that she was entirely in her place in encountering cold and snow on an errand of mercy, was much concerned at a young gentleman's getting his feet wet under a like impulse.

"You'd a deal better go back, sir," said Dolly, with respectful compassion. "You've no call to catch cold; and I'd ask you if you'd be so good as tell my husband to come, on your way back — he's at the Rainbow, I doubt — if you found him anyway sober enough to be o' use. Or else, there's Mrs. Snell 'ud happen send the boy up to fetch and carry, for there may be things wanted from the doctor's."

"No, I'll stay, now I'm once out; I'll stay outside here," said Godfrey, when they came opposite Marner's cottage. "You can come and tell me if I can do anything."

5   "Well, sir, you're very good; you've a tender heart," said Dolly, going to the door.

Godfrey was too painfully preoccupied to feel a twinge of self-reproach at this undeserved praise. He walked up and down, unconscious that he was plunging ankle 10 deep in snow, unconscious of everything but trembling suspense about what was going on in the cottage, and the effect of each alternative on his future lot. No, not quite unconscious of everything else. Deeper down, and half-smothered by passionate desire and dread, there was 15 the sense that he ought not to be waiting on these alternatives; that he ought to accept the consequences of his deeds, own the miserable wife, and fullfil the claims of the helpless child. But he had not moral courage enough to contemplate that active renunciation of Nancy as 20 possible for him; he had only conscience and heart enough to make him forever uneasy under the weakness that forbade the renunciation. And at this moment his mind leaped away from all restraint toward the sudden prospect of deliverance from his long bondage.

25   "Is she dead?" said the voice that predominated over every other within him. "If she is, I may marry Nancy; and then I shall be a good fellow in future and have no secrets, and the child — shall be taken care of somehow." But across that vision came the other possibility: "She 30 may live, and then it's all up with me."

Godfrey never knew how long it was before the door of the cottage opened and Mr. Kimble came out. He went forward to meet his uncle, prepared to suppress the agitation he must feel, whatever news he was to hear.

" I waited for you, as I'd come so far," he said, speaking first.

" Pooh, it was nonsense for you to come out; why didn't you send one of the men? There's nothing to be done. She's dead — has been dead for hours, I should say." 5

" What sort of woman is she?" said Godfrey, feeling the blood rush to his face.

" A young woman, but emaciated, with long black hair. Some vagrant — quite in rags. She's got a wedding-ring on, however. They must fetch her away to the workhouse to-morrow. Come, come along." 10

" I want to look at her," said Godfrey. " I think I saw such a woman yesterday. I'll overtake you in a minute or two." 15

Mr. Kimble went on, and Godfrey turned back to the cottage. He cast only one glance at the dead face on the pillow, which Dolly had smoothed with decent care; but he remembered that last look at his unhappy, hated wife so well that at the end of sixteen years every line in the worn face was present to him when he told the full story of this night. 20

He turned immediately towards the hearth, where Silas Marner sat lulling the child. She was perfectly quiet now, but not asleep — only soothed by sweet porridge and warmth into that wide-gazing calm which makes us older human beings, with our inward turmoil, feel a certain awe in the presence of a little child, such as we feel before some quiet majesty or beauty in the earth or sky — before a steady glowing planet, or a full-flowered eglantine, or the bending trees over a silent pathway. The wide-open blue eyes looked up at Godfrey's without any uneasiness or sign of recognition; the child could make no visible audible claim on its father, and the father 25 30

felt a strange mixture of feelings, a conflict of regret and
joy that the pulse of that little heart had no response for
the half-jealous yearning in his own, when the blue eyes
turned away from him slowly, and fixed themselves on the
5 weaver's queer face, which was bent low down to look
at them, while the small hand began to pull Marner's
withered cheek with loving disfiguration.

"You'll take the child to the parish to-morrow?" asked
Godfrey, speaking as indifferently as he could.

10   "Who says so?" said Marner sharply. "Will they
make me take her?"

"Why, you wouldn't like to keep her, should you —
an old bachelor like you?"

"Till anybody shows they've a right to take her away
15 from me," said Marner. "The mother's dead, and I
reckon it's got no father; it's a lone thing and I'm a
lone thing. My money's gone, I don't know where —
and this is come from I don't know where. I know
nothing — I'm partly mazed."

20   "Poor little thing!" said Godfrey. "Let me give
something towards finding it clothes."

He had put his hand in his pocket and found half a
guinea, and, thrusting it into Silas's hand, he hurried out
of the cottage to overtake Mr. Kimble.

25   "Ah, I see it's not the same woman I saw," he said,
as he came up. "It's a pretty little child; the old fellow
seems to want to keep it; that's strange for a miser like
him. But I gave him a trifle to help him out; the parish
isn't likely to quarrel with him for the right to keep the
30 child."

"No; but I've seen the time when I might have quar-
reled with him for it myself. It's too late now, though.
If the child ran into the fire, your aunt's too fat to over-
take it; she could only sit and grunt like an alarmed sow.

But what a fool you are, Godfrey, to come out in your dancing shoes and stockings in this way — and you one of the beaux of the evening, and at your own house! What do you mean by such freaks, young fellow? Has Miss Nancy been cruel, and do you want to spite her by spoiling your pumps?"

"Oh, everything has been disagreeable to-night. I was tired to death of jigging and gallanting and that bother about the hornpipes. And I'd got to dance with the other Miss Gunn," said Godfrey, glad of the subterfuge his uncle had suggested to him.

The prevarication and white lies which a mind that keeps itself ambitiously pure is as uneasy under as a great artist under the false touches that no eye detects but his own are worn as lightly as mere trimmings when once the actions have become a lie.

Godfrey reappeared in the white parlor with dry feet, and, since the truth must be told, with a sense of relief and gladness that was too strong for painful thoughts to struggle with. For could he not venture now, whenever opportunity offered, to say the tenderest things to Nancy Lammeter — to promise her and himself that he would always be just what she would desire to see him? There was no danger that his dead wife would be recognized; those were not days of active inquiry and wide report, and as for the registry of their marriage, that was a long way off, buried in unturned pages, away from every one's interest but his own. Dunsey might betray him if he came back; but Dunsey might be won to silence.

And when events turn out so much better for a man than he has had reason to dread, is it not a proof that his conduct has been less foolish and blameworthy than it might otherwise have appeared? When we are treated well, we naturally begin to think that we are not altogether

unmeritorious, and that it is only just we should treat
ourselves well, and not mar our own good fortune.
Where, after all, would be the use of his confessing the
past to Nancy Lammeter, and throwing away his happi-
5 ness? nay, hers? for he felt some confidence that she
loved him.　As for the child, he would see that it was
cared for; he would never forsake it; he would do
everything but own it.　Perhaps it would be just as happy
in life without being owned by its father, seeing that
10 nobody could tell how things would turn out, and that —
is there any other reason wanted? — well, then, that the
father would be much happier without owning the child.

CHAPTER XIV.

THERE was a pauper's burial that week in Raveloe, and up Kench Yard at Batherley it was known that the dark-haired woman with the fair child, who had lately come to lodge there, was gone away again. That was all the express note taken that Molly had disappeared from the eyes of men. But the unwept death which, to the general lot, seemed as trivial as the summer-shed leaf, was charged with the force of destiny to certain human lives that we know of, shaping their joys and sorrows even to the end.

Silas Marner's determination to keep the "tramp's child" was matter of hardly less surprise and iterated talk in the village than the robbery of his money. That softening of feeling towards him which dated from his misfortune, that merging of suspicion and dislike in a rather contemptuous pity for him as lone and crazy, was now accompanied with a more active sympathy, especially amongst the women. Notable mothers, who knew what it was to keep children "whole and sweet"; lazy mothers, who knew what it was to be interrupted in folding their arms and scratching their elbows by the mischievous propensities of children just firm on their legs, were equally interested in conjecturing how a lone man would manage with a two-year-old child on his hands, and were equally ready with their suggestions; the notable chiefly telling him what he had better do, and the lazy ones being emphatic in telling him what he would never be able to do.

Among the notable mothers, Dolly Winthrop was the one whose neighborly offices were the most acceptable to Marner, for they were rendered without any show of bus-

tling instruction.   Silas had shown her the half-guinea
given to him by Godfrey, and had asked her what he
should do about getting some clothes for the child.

" Eh, Master Marner," said Dolly, " there's no call to
5 buy no more nor a pair o' shoes ; for I've got the little
petticoats as Aaron wore five years ago, and it's ill spending the money on them baby clothes, for the child 'ull
grow like grass i' May, bless it — that it will."

And the same day Dolly brought her bundle, and dis-
10 played to Marner, one by one, the tiny garments in their
due order of succession, most of them patched and darned,
but clean and neat as fresh-sprung herbs.   This was the
introduction to a great ceremony with soap and water,
from which Baby came out in new beauty, and sat on Dol-
15 ly's knee, handling her toes and chuckling and patting
her palms together with an air of having made several
discoveries about herself, which she communicated by
alternate sounds of " gug-gug-gug " and " mammy."   The
" mammy " was not a cry of need or uneasiness ; Baby
20 had been used to utter it without expecting either tender
sound or touch to follow.

" Anybody 'ud think the angils in heaven couldn't be
prettier," said Dolly, rubbing the golden curls and kissing
them.   " And to think of its being covered wi' them dirty
25 rags, and the poor mother froze to death ; but there's
Them as took care of it and brought it to your door, Master Marner.   The door was open, and it walked in over
the snow, like as if it had been a little starved robin.
Didn't you say the door was open ? "

30   " Yes," said Silas meditatively.   " Yes — the door was
open.   The money's gone I don't know where, and this
is come from I don't know where."

He had not mentioned to any one his unconsciousness
of the child's entrance, shrinking from questions which

might lead to the fact he himself suspected, namely, that
he had been in one of his trances.

"Ah," said Dolly, with soothing gravity, "it's like the
night and the morning, and the sleeping and the waking,
and the rain and the harvest — one goes and the other
comes, and we know nothing how nor where. We may
strive and scrat and fend, but it's little we can do arter
all — the big things come and go wi' no striving o' our 'n
— they do, that they do; and I think you're in the right
on it to keep the little un, Master Marner, seeing as it's
been sent to you, though there's folks as thinks different.
You'll happen be a bit moithered with it while it's so
little; but I'll come, and welcome, and see to it for you.
I've a bit o' time to spare most days, for when one gets
up betimes i' the morning, the clock seems to stan' still
tow'rt ten, afore it's time to go about the victual. So, as
I say, I'll come and see to the child for you, and welcome."

"Thank you kindly," said Silas, hesitating a little.
"I'll be glad if you'll tell me things. But," he added
uneasily, leaning forward to look at Baby with some
jealousy, as she was resting her head backward against
Dolly's arm and eyeing him contentedly from a distance,
"but I want to do things for it myself, else it may get
fond o' somebody else, and not fond o' me. I've been
used to fending for myself in the house — I can learn, I
can learn."

"Eh, to be sure," said Dolly gently. "I've seen men
as are wonderful handy wi' children. The men are awk-
'ard and contrary mostly — God help 'em; but when the
drink's out of 'em, they are n't unsensible, though they're
bad for leeching and bandaging — so fiery and unpatient.
You see this goes first, next the skin," proceeded Dolly,
taking up the little shirt and putting it on.

"Yes," said Marner docilely, bringing his eyes very close, that they might be initiated in the mysteries; whereupon Baby seized his head with both her small arms and put her lips against his face with purring noises.

5   "See there," said Dolly, with a woman's tender tact, "she's fondest o' you. She wants to go o' your lap, I'll be bound. Go, then; take her, Master Marner. You can put the things on, and then you can say as you've done for her from the first of her coming to you."

10   Marner took her on his lap, trembling with an emotion mysterious to himself, at something unknown dawning on his life. Thought and feeling were so confused within him that, if he had tried to give them utterance, he could only have said that the child was come instead of the
15 gold — that the gold had turned into the child. He took the garments from Dolly and put them on under her teaching; interrupted, of course, by Baby's gymnastics.

"There, then! why, you take to it quite easy, Master Marner," said Dolly; "but what shall you do when you're
20 forced to sit in your loom? For she'll get busier and mischievouser every day — she will, bless her. It's lucky as you've got that high hearth i'stead of a grate, for that keeps the fire more out of her reach; but if you've got anything as can be spilt or broke, or as is fit to cut
25 her fingers off, she'll be at it, and it is but right you should know."

Silas meditated a little while in some perplexity. "I'll tie her to the leg o' the loom," he said at last, "tie her with a good long strip o' something."

30   "Well, mayhap that'll do, as it's a little gell, for they're easier persuaded to sit i' one place nor the lads. I know what the lads are; for I've had four — four I've had, God knows — and if you was to take and tie 'em up, they'd make a fighting and a crying as if you was ringing

the pigs. But I'll bring you my little chair and some
bits o' red rag and things for her to play wi', an' she'll
sit and chatter to 'em as if they was alive. Eh, if it
was n't a sin to the lads to wish 'em made different, bless
'em, I should ha' been glad for one of 'em to be a little   5
gell; and to think as I could ha' taught her to scour and
mend and the knitting and everything. But I can teach
'em this little un, Master Marner, when she gets old
enough."

"But she'll be *my* little un," said Marner, rather has-   10
tily. "She'll be nobody else's."

"No, to be sure; you'll have a right to her, if you're
a father to her, and bring her up according. But," added
Dolly, coming to a point which she had determined beforehand to touch upon, "you must bring her up like   15
christened folks's children, and take her to church, and
let her learn her catechise, as my little Aaron can say
off — the 'I believe,' and everything, and 'hurt nobody
by word or deed,' — as well as if he was the clerk. That's
what you must do, Master Marner, if you'd do the right   20
thing by the orphin child."

Marner's pale face flushed suddenly under a new
anxiety. His mind was too busy trying to give some
definite bearing to Dolly's words for him to think of
answering her.   25

"And it's my belief," she went on, "as the poor little
creature has never been christened, and it's nothing but
right as the parson should be spoke to; and if you was
noways unwilling, I'd talk to Mr. Macey about it this
very day. For if the child ever went anyways wrong, and   30
you had n't done your part by it, Master Marner — 'noculation and everything to save it from harm — it 'ud be a
thorn i' your bed forever o' this side the grave; and I
can't think as it 'ud be easy lying down for anybody when

they'd got to another world if they hadn't done their part by the helpless children as come wi'out their own asking."

Dolly herself was disposed to be silent for some time now, for she had spoken from the depths of her own simple belief, and was much concerned to know whether her words would produce the desired effect on Silas. He was puzzled and anxious, for Dolly's word "christened" conveyed no distinct meaning to him. He had only heard of baptism, and had only seen the baptism of grown-up men and women.

"What is it as you mean by 'christened'?" he said at last timidly. "Won't folks be good to her without it?"

"Dear, dear! Master Marner," said Dolly, with gentle distress and compassion. "Had you never no father nor mother as taught you to say your prayers, and as there's good words and good things to keep us from harm?"

"Yes," said Silas, in a low voice; "I know a deal about that — used to, used to. But your ways are different: my country was a good way off." He paused a few moments, and then added more decidedly, "But I want to do everything as can be done for the child. And whatever's right for it i' this country, and you think 'ull do it good, I'll act according, if you'll tell me."

"Well, then, Master Marner," said Dolly, inwardly rejoiced, "I'll ask Mr. Macey to speak to the parson about it; and you must fix on a name for it, because it must have a name giv' it when it's christened."

"My mother's name was Hephzibah," said Silas, "and my little sister was named after her."

"Eh, that's a hard name," said Dolly. "I partly think it isn't a christened name."

"It's a Bible name," said Silas, old ideas recurring.

"Then I've no call to speak again' it," said Dolly,

rather startled by Silas's knowledge on this head; "but you see I'm no scholar, and I'm slow at catching the words. My husband says I'm allays like as if I was putting the haft for the handle — that's what he says — for he's very sharp, God help him. But it was awk'ard calling your little sister by such a hard name, when you'd got nothing big to say, like — wasn't it, Master Marner?"

"We called her Eppie," said Silas.

"Well, if it was noways wrong to shorten the name, it 'ud be a deal handier. And so I'll go now, Master Marner, and I'll speak about the christening afore dark; and I wish you the best o' luck, and it's my belief as it'll come to you, if you do what's right by the orphin child; — and there's the 'noculation to be seen to; and as to washing its bits o' things, you need look to nobody but me, for I can do 'em wi' one hand when I've got my suds about. Eh, the blessed angil! You'll let me bring my Aaron one o' these days, and he'll show her his little cart as his father's made for him, and the black-and-white pup as he's got a-rearing."

Baby *was* christened, the rector deciding that a double baptism was the lesser risk to incur; and on this occasion Silas, making himself as clean and tidy as he could, appeared for the first time within the church, and shared in the observances held sacred by his neighbors. He was quite unable, by means of anything he heard or saw, to identify the Raveloe religion with his old faith; if he could at any time in his previous life have done so, it must have been by the aid of a strong feeling ready to vibrate with sympathy, rather than by a comparison of phrases and ideas; and now for long years that feeling had been dormant. He had no distinct idea about the baptism and the church-going, except that Dolly had said it was for the good of the child; and in this way, as the

weeks grew to months, the child created fresh and fresh
links between his life and the lives from which he had
hitherto shrink continually into narrower isolation. Unlike
the gold which needed nothing, and must be worshipped
5 in close-locked solitude — which was hidden away from
the daylight, was deaf to the song of birds, and started to
no human tones — Eppie was a creature of endless claims
and ever-growing desires, seeking and loving sunshine,
and living sounds, and living movements; making trial of
10 everything, with trust in new joy, and stirring the human
kindness in all eyes that looked on her. The gold had
kept his thoughts in an ever-repeated circle, leading to
nothing beyond itself; but Eppie was an object com-
pacted of changes and hopes that forced his thoughts
15 onward, and carried them far away from their old eager
pacing towards the same blank limit — carried them away
to the new things that would come with the coming years,
when Eppie would have learned to understand how her
father Silas cared for her; and made him look for images
20 of that time in the ties and charities that bound together
the families of his neighbors. The gold had asked that
he should sit weaving longer and longer, deafened and
blinded more and more to all things except the monotony
of his loom and the repetition of his web; but Eppie called
25 him away from his weaving, and made him think all its
pauses a holiday, reawakening his senses with her fresh
life, even to the old winter flies that came crawling forth
in the early spring sunshine, and warming him into joy
because *she* had joy.

30   And when the sunshine grew strong and lasting, so
that the buttercups were thick in the meadows, Silas
might be seen in the sunny midday, or in the late afternoon when the shadows were lengthening under the hedgerows, strolling out with uncovered head to carry Eppie

beyond the Stone-pits to where the flowers grew, till they reached some favorite bank where he could sit down, while Eppie toddled to pluck the flowers and make remarks to the winged things that murmured happily above the bright petals, calling " Dad-dad's " attention continually by bringing him the flowers. Then she would turn her ear to some sudden bird note, and Silas learned to please her by making signs of hushed stillness, that they might listen for the note to come again; so that when it came, she set up her small back and laughed with gurgling triumph. Sitting on the banks in this way, Silas began to look for the once familiar herbs again; and as the leaves, with their unchanged outline and markings, lay on his palm, there was a sense of crowding remembrances from which he turned away timidly, taking refuge in Eppie's little world, that lay lightly on his enfeebled spirit.

As the child's mind was growing into knowledge, his mind was growing into memory; as her life unfolded, his soul, long stupefied in a cold, narrow prison, was unfolding, too, and trembling gradually into full consciousness.

It was an influence which must gather force with every new year; the tones that stirred Silas's heart grew articulate, and called for more distinct answers; shapes and sounds grew clearer for Eppie's eyes and ears, and there was more that " Dad-dad " was imperatively required to notice and account for. Also, by the time Eppie was three years old, she developed a fine capacity for mischief, and for devising ingenious ways of being troublesome, which found much exercise, not only for Silas's patience, but for his watchfulness and penetration. Sorely was poor Silas puzzled on such occasions by the incompatible demands of love. Dolly Winthrop told him that punishment was good for Eppie, and that, as for rearing a child without making it tingle a little in soft and safe places now and then, it was not to be done.

"To be sure, there's another thing you might do, Master Marner," added Dolly meditatively, "you might shut her up once i' the coal hole. That was what I did wi' Aaron; for I was that silly wi' the youngest lad as I could never bear to smack him. Not as I could find i' my heart to let him stay i' the coal hole more nor a minute, but it was enough to colly him all over, so as he must be new washed and dressed, and it was as good as a rod to him — that was. But I put it upo' your conscience, Master Marner, as there's one of 'em you must choose — ayther smacking or the coal hole — else she'll get so masterful there 'll be no holding her."

Silas was impressed with the melancholy truth of this last remark; but his force of mind failed before the only two penal methods open to him, not only because it was painful to him to hurt Eppie, but because he trembled at a moment's contention with her, lest she should love him the less for it. Let even an affectionate Goliath get himself tied to a small, tender thing, dreading to hurt it by pulling, and dreading still more to snap the cord, and which of the two, pray, will be master? It was clear that Eppie, with her short, toddling steps, must lead father Silas a pretty dance on any fine morning when circumstances favored mischief.

For example. He had wisely chosen a broad strip of linen as a means of fastening her to his loom when he was busy; it made a broad belt round her waist, and was long enough to allow of her reaching the truckle-bed and sitting down on it, but not long enough for her to attempt any dangerous climbing. One bright summer's morning Silas had been more engrossed than usual in "setting up" a new piece of work, an occasion on which his scissors

were in requisition. These scissors, owing to an especial
warning of Dolly's, had been kept carefully out of Eppie's
reach ; but the click of them had had a peculiar attraction
for her ear, and, watching the results of that click, she
had derived the philosophic lesson that the same cause
would produce the same effect. Silas had seated himself
in his loom, and the noise of weaving had begun; but he
had left his scissors on a ledge which Eppie's arm was long
enough to reach ; and now, like a small mouse, watching
her opportunity, she stole quietly from her corner, secured
the scissors, and toddled to the bed again, setting up her
back as a mode of concealing the fact. She had a distinct
intention as to the use of the scissors ; and having cut the
linen strip in a jagged but effectual manner, in two moments
she had run out at the open door where the sunshine was
inviting her, while poor Silas believed her to be a better
child than usual. It was not until he happened to need
his scissors that the terrible fact burst upon him — Eppie
had run out by herself — had perhaps fallen into the Stone-
pit. Silas, shaken by the worst fear that could have be-
fallen him, rushed out, calling " Eppie ! " and ran eagerly
about the uninclosed space, exploring the dry cavities into
which she might have fallen, and then gazing with questioning dread at the smooth, red surface of the water. The
cold drops stood on his brow. How long had she been
out? There was one hope — that she had crept through
the stile and got into the fields, where he habitually took
her to stroll. But the grass was high in the meadow, and
there was no descrying her, if she were there, except by a
close search that would be a trespass on Mr. Osgood's
crop. Still, that misdemeanor must be committed; and
poor Silas, after peering all round the hedgerows, trav-
ersed the grass, beginning with perturbed vision to see
Eppie behind every group of red sorrel, and to see her

moving always farther off as he approached.   The meadow
was searched in vain; and he got over the stile into the
next field, looking with dying hope towards a small pond
which was now reduced to its summer shallowness, so as
5 to leave a wide margin of good adhesive mud.   Here,
however, sat Eppie, discoursing cheerfully to her own small
boot, which she was using as a bucket to convey the water
into a deep hoof-mark, while her little naked foot was
planted comfortably on a cushion of olive green mud.   A
10 red-headed calf was observing her with alarmed doubt
through the opposite hedge.

Here was clearly a case of aberration in a christened
child which demanded severe treatment; but Silas, overcome with convulsive joy at finding his treasure again,
15 could do nothing but snatch her up and cover her with
half-sobbing kisses.   It was not until he had carried her
home, and had begun to think of the necessary washing,
that he recollected the need that he should punish Eppie,
and "make her remember."   The idea that she might run
20 away again and come to harm gave him unusual resolution, and for the first time he determined to try the coal
hole, — a small closet near the hearth.

"Naughty, naughty Eppie," he suddenly began, holding her on his knee and pointing to her muddy feet and
25 clothes ; "naughty to cut with the scissors and run away.
Eppie must go into the coal hole for being naughty.   Daddy
must put her in the coal hole."

He half-expected that this would be shock enough and
that Eppie would begin to cry.   But, instead of that, she
30 began to shake herself on his knee, as if the proposition
opened a pleasing novelty.   Seeing that he must proceed
to extremities, he put her into the coal hole, and held the
door closed, with a trembling sense that he was using a
strong measure.   For a moment there was silence, but

then came a little cry, " Opy, opy !" and Silas let her out again, saying, " Now Eppie 'ull never be naughty again, else she must go into the coal hole, — a black, naughty place."

The weaving must stand still a long while this morning, for now Eppie must be washed and have clean clothes on ; but it was to be hoped that this punishment would have a lasting effect and save time in future — though, perhaps, it would have been better if Eppie had cried more.

In half an hour she was clean again, and Silas, having turned his back to see what he could do with the linen band, threw it down again, with the reflection that Eppie would be good without fastening for the rest of the morning. He turned round again, and was going to place her in her little chair near the loom, when she peeped out at him with black face and hands again, and said, " Eppie in de toal hole !"

This total failure of the coal-hole discipline shook Silas's belief in the efficacy of punishment. " She 'd take it all for fun," he observed to Dolly, " if I did n't hurt her, and that I can't do, Mrs. Winthrop. If she makes me a bit o' trouble, I can bear it. And she 's got no tricks but what she 'll grow out of."

" Well, that 's partly true, Master Marner," said Dolly sympathetically ; " and if you can't bring your mind to frighten her off touching things, you must do what you can to keep 'em out of her way. That 's what I do wi' the pups as the lads are allays a-rearing. They *will* worry and gnaw — worry and gnaw they will, if it was one's Sunday cap as hung anywhere so they could drag it. They know no difference — God help 'em ; it 's the pushing o' the teeth as sets 'em on, that 's what it is."

So Eppie was reared without punishment, the burden of her misdeeds being borne vicariously by father Silas.

The stone hut was made a soft nest for her, lined with downy patience; and also in the world that lay beyond the stone hut she knew nothing of frowns and denials.

Notwithstanding the difficulty of carrying her and his yarn or linen at the same time, Silas took her with him in most of his journeys to the farmhouses, unwilling to leave her behind at Dolly Winthrop's, who was always ready to take care of her; and little curly-headed Eppie, the weaver's child, became an object of interest at several outlying homesteads, as well as in the village. Hitherto he had been treated very much as if he had been a useful gnome or brownie, — a queer and unaccountable creature, who must necessarily be looked at with wondering curiosity and repulsion, and with whom one would be glad to make all greetings and bargains as brief as possible, but who must be dealt with in a propitiatory way, and occasionally have a present of pork or garden stuff to carry home with him, seeing that without him there was no getting the yarn woven. But now Silas met with open, smiling faces and cheerful questioning, as a person whose satisfaction and difficulties could be understood. Everywhere he must sit a little and talk about the child, and words of interest were always ready for him : "Ah, Master Marner, you'll be lucky if she takes the measles soon and easy !" or, "Why, there isn't many lone men 'ud ha' been wishing to take up with a little un like that; but I reckon the weaving makes you handier than men as do outdoor work — you're partly as handy as a woman, for weaving comes next to spinning." Elderly masters and mistresses, seated observantly in large kitchen armchairs, shook their heads over the difficulties attendant on rearing children, felt Eppie's round arms and legs, and pronounced them remarkably firm, and told Silas that if she turned out well (which, however, there was no telling), it

would be a fine thing for him to have a steady lass to
do for him when he got helpless. Servant maidens
were fond of carrying her out to look at the hens and
chickens or to see if any cherries could be shaken
down in the orchard; and the small boys and girls 5
approached her slowly, with cautious movement and
steady gaze, like little dogs face to face with one of their
own kind, till attraction had reached the point at which
the soft lips were put out for a kiss. No child was afraid
of approaching Silas when Eppie was near him; there 10
was no repulsion around him now, either for young or
old, for the little child had come to link him once more
with the whole world. There was love between him and
the child that blent them into one, and there was love
between the child and the world, — from men and women 15
with parental looks and tones to the red ladybirds and
the round pebbles.

Silas began now to think of Raveloe life entirely in
relation to Eppie; she must have everything that was good
in Raveloe; and he listened docilely, that he might come 20
to understand better what this life was, from which, for
fifteen years, he had stood aloof as from a strange thing,
wherewith he could have no communion; as some man
who has a precious plant to which he would give a nurtur-
ing home in a new soil thinks of the rain and the sun- 25
shine and all influences in relation to his nursling, and
asks industriously for all knowledge that will help him to
satisfy the wants of the searching roots or to guard leaf
and bud from invading harm. The disposition to hoard
had been utterly crushed at the very first by the loss of 30
his long-stored gold; the coins he earned afterwards
seemed as irrelevant as stones brought to complete a
house suddenly buried by an earthquake; the sense of
bereavement was too heavy upon him for the old thrill of

satisfaction to arise again at the touch of the newly earned coin. And now something had come to replace his hoard which gave a growing purpose to the earnings, drawing his hope and joy continually onward beyond the money.

5 In old days there were angels who came and took men by the hand and led them away from the city of destruction. We see no white-winged angels now. But yet men are led away from threatening destruction ; a hand is put into theirs, which leads them forth gently towards a calm 10 and bright land, so that they look no more backward— and the hand may be a little child's.

CHAPTER XV.

THERE was one person, as you will believe, who watched with keener, though more hidden, interest than any other the prosperous growth of Eppie under the weaver's care. He dared not do anything that would imply a stronger interest in a poor man's adopted child than could be expected from the kindliness of the young Squire, when a chance meeting suggested a little present to a simple old fellow whom others noticed with good will ; but he told himself that the time would come when he might do something towards furthering the welfare of his daughter without incurring suspicion. Was he very uneasy in the meantime at his inability to give his daughter her birthright ? I cannot say that he was. The child was being taken care of, and would very likely be happy, as people in humble stations often were — happier, perhaps, than those brought up in luxury.

That famous ring that pricked its owner when he forgot duty and followed desire — I wonder if it pricked very hard when he set out on the chase, or whether it pricked but lightly then, and only pierced to the quick when the chase had long been ended, and hope, folding her wings, looked backward and became regret ?

Godfrey Cass's cheek and eye were brighter than ever now. He was so undivided in his aims that he seemed like a man of firmness. No Dunsey had come back ; people had made up their minds that he was gone for a soldier, or gone " out of the country," and no one cared to be specific in their inquiries on a subject delicate to a respectable family. Godfrey had ceased to see the shadow of Dunsey across his path ; and the path now lay straight

forward to the accomplishment of his best, longest-cherished wishes.   Everybody said Mr. Godfrey had taken the right turn ; and it was pretty clear what would be the end of things, for there were not many days in the week that
5 he was not seen riding to the Warrens.   Godfrey himself, when he was asked jocosely if the day had been fixed, smiled with the pleasant consciousness of a lover who could say " yes " if he liked.   He felt a reformed man, delivered from temptation ; and the vision of his future
10 life seemed to him as a promised land for which he had no cause to fight.   He saw himself with all his happiness centered on his own hearth, while Nancy would smile on him as he played with the children.

And that other child, not on the hearth — he would not
15 forget it ; he would see that it was well provided for. That was a father's duty.

PART II.

CHAPTER XVI.

IT was a bright autumn Sunday, sixteen years after Silas Marner had found his new treasure on the hearth. The bells of the old Raveloe church were ringing the cheerful peal that told that the morning service was ended; and out of the arched doorway in the tower came slowly, retarded by friendly greetings and questions, the richer parishioners who had chosen this bright Sunday morning as eligible for church-going. It was the rural fashion of that time for the more important members of the congregation to depart first, while their humbler neighbors waited and looked on, stroking their bent heads or dropping their curtsies to any large ratepayer who turned to notice them.

Foremost among these advancing groups of well-clad people there are some whom we shall recognize, in spite of Time, who has laid his hand on them all. The tall blonde man of forty is not much changed in features from the Godfrey Cass of six and twenty; he is only fuller in flesh, and has only lost the indefinable look of youth, — a loss which is marked even when the eye is undulled and the wrinkles are not yet come. Perhaps the pretty woman, not much younger than he, who is leaning on his arm, is more changed than her husband; the lovely bloom that used to be always on her cheek now comes but fitfully, with the fresh morning air or with some strong surprise; yet to all who love human faces best for what they

tell of human experience, Nancy's beauty has a heightened
interest.   Often the soul is ripened into fuller goodness
while age has spread an ugly film, so that mere glances can
never divine the preciousness of the fruit.   But the years
5 have not been so cruel to Nancy.   The firm yet placid
mouth, the clear, veracious glance of the brown eyes speak
now of a nature that has been tested and has kept its
highest qualities ; and even the costume, with its dainty
neatness and purity, has more significance now the co-
10 quetries of youth can have nothing to do with it.

Mr. and Mrs. Godfrey Cass (any higher title has died
away from Raveloe lips since the old Squire was gathered
to his fathers and his inheritance was divided) have turned
round to look for the tall, aged man and the plainly dressed
15 woman who are a little behind— Nancy having observed
that they must wait for "father and Priscilla"— and now
they all turn into a narrower path leading across the
churchyard to a small gate opposite the Red House.   We
will not follow them now ; for may there not be some
20 others in this departing congregation whom we should
like to see again,— some of those who are not likely to be
handsomely clad, and whom we may not recognize so easily
as the master and mistress of the Red House ?

But it is impossible to mistake Silas Marner.   His large
25 brown eyes seem to have gathered a longer vision, as is the
way with eyes that have been short-sighted in early life,
and they have a less vague, a more answering gaze ; but in
everything else one sees signs of a frame much enfeebled
by the lapse of the sixteen years.   The weaver's bent shoul-
30 ders and white hair give him almost the look of advanced
age, though he is not more than five and fifty ; but there
is the freshest blossom of youth close by his side,— a blonde,
dimpled girl of eighteen, who has vainly tried to chastise
her curly auburn hair into smoothness under her brown

bonnet; the hair ripples as obstinately as a brooklet under the March breeze, and the little ringlets burst away from the restraining comb behind and show themselves below the bonnet crown. Eppie cannot help being rather vexed about her hair, for there is no other girl in Raveloe who 5 has hair at all like it, and she thinks hair ought to be smooth. She does not like to be blameworthy even in small things ; you see how neatly her prayer-book is folded in her spotted handkerchief.

That good-looking young fellow in a new fustian suit 10 who walks behind her is not quite sure upon the question of hair in the abstract, when Eppie puts it to him, and thinks that perhaps straight hair is the best in general, but he does n't want Eppie's hair to be different. She surely divines that there is some one behind her who is thinking 15 about her very particularly and mustering courage to come to her side as soon as they are out in the lane, else why should she look rather shy and take care not to turn away her head from her father Silas, to whom she keeps murmuring little sentences as to who was at church and 20 who was not at church, and how pretty the red mountain ash is over the rectory wall !

" I wish *we* had a little garden, father, with double daisies in it, like Mrs. Winthrop's, " said Eppie, when they were out in the lane ; " only they say it 'ud take a deal of 25 digging and bringing fresh soil — and you could n't do that, could you, father ? Anyhow, I should n't like you to do it, for it 'ud be too hard work for you."

" Yes, I could do it, child, if you want a bit o' garden ; these long evenings I could work at taking in a little bit 30 o' the waste, just enough for a root or two o' flowers for you, and again i' the morning I could have a turn wi' the spade before I sat down to the loom. Why did n't you tell me before as you wanted a bit o' garden ? "

"*I* can dig it for you, Master Marner," said the young man in fustian, who was now by Eppie's side, entering into the conversation without the trouble of formalities. "It'll be play to me after I've done my day's work, or any odd
5 bits o' time when the work's slack. And I'll bring you some soil from Mr. Cass's garden — he'll let me, and willing."

"Eh, Aaron, my lad, are you there?" said Silas; "I was n't aware of you; for when Eppie's talking o' things
10 I see nothing but what she's a-saying. Well, if you could help me with the digging, we might get her a bit o' garden all the sooner."

"Then, if you think well and good," said Aaron, "I'll come to the Stone-pits this afternoon, and we'll settle
15 what land's to be taken in, and I'll get up an hour earlier i' the morning and begin on it."

"But not if you don't promise me not to work at the hard digging, father," said Eppie. "For I should n't ha' said anything about it," she added, half-bashfully, half-
20 roguishly, "only Mrs. Winthrop said as Aaron 'ud be so good, and —"

"And you might ha' known it without her telling you," said Aaron. "And Master Marner knows, too, I hope, as I'm able and willing to do a turn o' work for him, and he
25 won't do me the unkindness to anyways take it out o' my hands."

"There, now, father, you won't work in it till it's all easy," said Eppie, "and you and me can mark out the beds and make holes and plant the roots. It'll be a deal livelier
30 at the Stone-pits when we've got some flowers, for I always think the flowers can see us and know what we're talking about. And I'll have a bit of rosemary and bergamot and thyme, because they're so sweet-smelling; but there's no lavender only in the gentlefolks' gardens, I think."

" That 's no reason why you should n't have some," said Aaron, " for I can bring you slips of anything ; I 'm forced to cut no end of 'em when I 'm gardening, and I throw 'em away mostly. There 's a big bed o' lavender at the Red House ; the missis is very fond of it." 5

" Well," said Silas gravely, " so as you don't make free for us or ask for anything as is worth much at the Red House ; for Mr. Cass 's been so good to us, and built us up the new end o' the cottage and given us beds and things, as I could n't abide to be imposin' for garden stuff or any- 10 thing else."

" No, no, there 's no imposin'," said Aaron; " there 's never a garden in all the parish but what there 's endless waste in it for want o' somebody as could use everything up. It 's what I think to myself sometimes, as there 15 need nobody run short o' victuals if the land was made the most on, and there was never a morsel but what could find its way to a mouth. It sets one thinking o' that — gardening does. But I must go back now, else mother 'ull be in trouble as I are n't there." 20

" Bring her with you this afternoon, Aaron," said Eppie ; " I should n't like to fix about the garden and her not know everything from the first — should *you*, father ? "

" Ay, bring her if you can, Aaron," said Silas; " she 's 25 sure to have a word to say as 'll help us to set things on their right end."

Aaron turned back up the village, while Silas and Eppie went on up the lonely sheltered lane.

" O daddy!" she began, when they were in privacy, 30 clasping and squeezing Silas's arm, and skipping round to give him an energetic kiss. " My little old daddy ! I 'm so glad. I don't think I shall want anything else when we 've got a little garden ; and I knew Aaron would dig it for us," she went on with roguish triumph. "I knew that very well."

"You're a deep little puss, you are," said Silas, with the mild, passive happiness of love-crowned age in his
5 face; "but you'll make yourself fine and beholden to Aaron."

"Oh, no, I sha'n't," said Eppie, laughing and frisking; "he likes it."

"Come, come, let me carry your prayer-book, else
10 you'll be dropping it, jumping i' that way."

Eppie was now aware that her behavior was under observation, but it was only the observation of a friendly donkey, browsing with a log fastened to his foot, — a meek donkey, not scornfully critical of human trivialities, but
15 thankful to share in them, if possible, by getting his nose scratched ; and Eppie did not fail to gratify him with her usual notice, though it was attended with the inconvenience of his following them, painfully, up to the very door of their home.

20 But the sound of a sharp bark inside, as Eppie put the key in the door, modified the donkey's views, and he limped away again without bidding. The sharp bark was the sign of an excited welcome that was awaiting them from a knowing brown terrier, who, after dancing at their
25 legs in a hysterical manner, rushed with a worrying noise at a tortoise-shell kitten under the loom, and then rushed back with a sharp bark again, as much as to say, "I have done my duty by this feeble creature, you perceive" ; while the lady mother of the kitten sat sunning her white
30 bosom in the window, and looked round with a sleepy air of expecting caresses, though she was not going to take any trouble for them.

The presence of this happy animal life was not the only change which had come over the interior of the

stone cottage.   There was no bed now in the living room,
and the small space was well filled with decent furniture,
all bright and clean enough to satisfy Dolly Winthrop's
eye.   The oaken table and three-cornered oaken chair
were hardly what was likely to be seen in so poor a cot-   5
tage ; they had come, with the beds and other things, from
the Red House ; for Mr. Godfrey Cass, as every one said
in the village, did very kindly by the weaver ; and it was
nothing but right a man should be looked on and helped
by those who could afford it, when he had brought up an 10
orphan child and been father and mother to her, and
had lost his money, too, so as he had nothing but what he
worked for week by week, and when the weaving was
going down; too — for there was less and less flax spun —
and Master Marner was none so young.   Nobody was 15
jealous of the weaver, for he was regarded as an exceptional person, whose claims on neighborly help were not
to be matched in Raveloe.   Any superstition that remained concerning him had taken an entirely new color ;
and Mr. Macey, now a very feeble old man of fourscore 20
and six, never seen except in his chimney corner or sitting in the sunshine at his door-sill, was of opinion that
when a man had done what Silas had done by an orphan
child it was a sign that his money would come to light
again, or, leastwise, that the robber would be made to 25
answer for it — for, as Mr. Macey observed of himself,
his faculties were as strong as ever.

Silas sat down now and watched Eppie with a satisfied
gaze as she spread the clean cloth and set on it the potato
pie, warmed up slowly in a safe Sunday fashion, by being 30
put into a dry pot over a slowly dying fire, as the best
substitute for an oven.   For Silas would not consent to
have a grate and oven added to his conveniences ; he
loved the old brick hearth as he had loved his brown pot

— and was it not there when he had found Eppie? (The gods of the hearth exist for us still;) and let all new faith be tolerant of that fetishism, lest it bruise its own roots.

Silas ate his dinner more silently than usual, soon laying down his knife and fork, and watching half-abstractedly Eppie's play with Snap and the cat, by which her own dinner was made rather a lengthy business. Yet it was a sight that might well arrest wandering thoughts : Eppie, with the rippling radiance of her hair and the whiteness of her rounded chin and throat set off by the dark blue cotton gown, laughing merrily as the kitten held on with her four claws to one shoulder, like a design for a jug handle, while Snap on the right hand and Puss on the other put up their paws towards a morsel which she held out of the reach of both — Snap occasionally desisting in order to remonstrate with the cat by a cogent worrying growl on the greediness and futility of her conduct — till Eppie relented, caressed them both, and divided the morsel between them.

But at last Eppie, glancing at the clock, checked the play and said, "O daddy, you're wanting to go into the sunshine to smoke your pipe. But I must clear away first, so as the house may be tidy when godmother comes. I'll make haste — I won't be long."

Silas had taken to smoking a pipe daily during the last two years, having been strongly urged to it by the sages of Raveloe as a practice "good for the fits"; and this advice was sanctioned by Dr. Kimball, on the ground that it was as well to try what could do no harm, — a principle which was made to answer for a great deal of work in that gentleman's medical practice. Silas did not highly enjoy smoking, and often wondered how his neighbors could be so fond of it ; but a humble sort of acquiescence in what was held to be good had become a strong habit of that

new self which had been developed in him since he had
found Eppie on his hearth. It had been the only clue
his bewildered mind could hold by in cherishing this
young life that had been sent to him out of the darkness
into which his gold had departed. By seeking what was 5
needful for Eppie, by sharing the effect that everything
produced on her, he had himself come to appropriate the
forms of custom and belief which were the mold of
Raveloe life ; and as with reawakening sensibilities memory also reawakened, he had begun to ponder over the 10
elements of his old faith and blend them with his new
impressions, till he recovered a consciousness of unity between his past and present. The sense of presiding goodness and the human trust which come with all pure peace
and joy had given him a dim impression that there had 15
been some error, some mistake, which had thrown that
dark shadow over the days of his best years ; and as it
grew more and more easy to him to open his mind to
Dolly Winthrop, he gradually communicated to her all he
could describe of his early life. The communication was 20
necessarily a slow and difficult process, for Silas's meager
power of explanation was not aided by any readiness of
interpretation in Dolly, whose narrow outward experience
gave her no key to strange customs, and made every novelty a source of wonder that arrested them at every step 25
of the narrative. It was only by fragments, and at intervals which left Dolly time to revolve what she had heard
till it acquired some familiarity for her, that Silas at last
arrived at the climax of the sad story, — the drawing of
lots and its false testimony concerning him ; and this had 30
to be repeated in several interviews, under new questions
on her part as to the nature of his plan for detecting the
guilty and clearing the innocent.

"And yourn 's the same Bible, you 're sure o' that, Master Marner — the Bible as you brought wi' you from that country — it's the same as what they've got at church, and what Eppie's a-learning to read in?"

"Yes," said Silas, "every bit the same; and there's drawing o' lots in the Bible, mind you," he added in a lower tone.

"Oh, dear, dear," said Dolly in a grieved voice, as if she were hearing an unfavorable report of a sick man's case. She was silent for some minutes; at last she said: "There's wise folks, happen, as know how it all is — the parson knows, I'll be bound; but it takes big words to tell them things, and such as poor folks can't make much out on. I can never rightly know the meaning o' what I hear at church, only a bit here and there, but I know it's good words — I do. But what lies upo' your mind — it's this, Master Marner: as, if Them above had done the right thing by you, They'd never ha' let you be turned out for a wicked thief when you was innicent."

"Ah!" said Silas, who had now come to understand Dolly's phraseology, "that was what fell on me as if it had been red-hot iron; because, you see, there was nobody as cared for me or clave to me above nor below. And him as I'd gone out and in wi' for ten year and more, since when we was lads, and went halves — mine own familiar friend in whom I trusted — had lifted up his heel again' me and worked to ruin me."

"Eh, but he was a bad un — I can't think as there's another such," said Dolly. "But I'm o'ercome, Master Marner; I'm like as if I'd waked and did n't know whether it was night or morning. I feel somehow as sure as I do when I've laid something up, though I can't justly put my hand on it, as there was a rights in what happened to you, if one could but make it out; and you'd no call to lose heart as you did. But we'll talk on it again;

for sometimes things come into my head when I 'm leeching or poulticing or such as I could never think on when
I was sitting still."

Dolly was too useful a woman not to have many opportunities of illumination of the kind she alluded to, and 5
she was not long before she recurred to the subject.

"Master Marner," she said, one day that she came to
bring home Eppie's washing, "I 've been sore puzzled for
a good bit wi' that trouble o' yourn and the drawing o'
lots; and it got twisted back'ards and for'ards, as I 10
didn't know which end to lay hold on. But it come to
me all clear like that night when I was sitting up wi' poor
Bessy Fawkes, as is dead and left her children behind —
God help 'em — it come to me as clear as daylight; but
whether I 've got hold on it now or can anyways bring it 15
to my tongue's end, that I don't know. For I 've often a
deal inside me as 'll never come out; and for what you
talk o' your folks in your old country niver saying prayers
by heart nor saying 'em out of a book, they must be
wonderful clever; for if I didn't know 'Our Father' and 20
little bits o' good words as I can carry out o' church wi'
me, I might down o' my knees every night, but nothing
could I say."

"But you can mostly say something as I can make sense
on, Mrs. Winthrop," said Silas. 25

"Well, then, Master Marner, it come to me summat like
this: I can make nothing o' the drawing o' lots and the
answer coming wrong; it 'ud mayhap take the parson to
tell that, and he could only tell us i' big words. But what
come to me as clear as the daylight — it was when I was 30
troubling over poor Bessy Fawkes, and it allays comes into
my head when I 'm sorry for folks and feel as I can't do
a power to help 'em, not if I was to get up i' the middle
o' the night — it comes into my head as Them above has

got a deal tenderer heart nor what I've got—for I can't
be anyways better nor Them as made me; and if anything
looks hard to me, it's because there's things I don't know
on; and for the matter o' that, there may be plenty
5 o' things I don't know on, for it's little as I know—
that it is. And so, while I was thinking o' that, you
come into my mind, Master Marner, and it all come
pouring in: if *I* felt i' my inside what was the right
and just thing by you, and them as prayed and
10 drawed the lots, all but that wicked un, if *they*'d ha'
done the right thing by you if they could, isn't there
Them as was at the making on us, and knows better
and has a better will? And that's all as ever I can be
sure on, and everything else is a big puzzle to me when I
15 think on it. For there was the fever come and took off
them as were full-growed and left the helpless children;
and there's the breaking o' limbs; and them as 'ud do
right and be sober have to suffer by them as are contrary
—eh, there's trouble i' this world, and there's things as
20 we can niver make out the rights on. And all as we've
got to do is to trusten, Master Marner—to do the right
thing as fur as we know, and to trusten. For if us as
knows so little can see a bit o' good and rights, we may
be sure as there's a good and a rights bigger nor what
25 we can know—I feel it i' my own inside as it must be so.
And if you could but ha' gone on trustening, Master Marner, you wouldn't ha' run away from your fellow-creatures
and been so lone."

"Ah, but that 'ud ha' been hard," said Silas, in an under-
30 tone; "it 'ud ha' been hard to trusten then."

"And so it would," said Dolly, almost with compunction; "them things are easier said nor done, and I'm
partly ashamed o' talking."

"Nay, nay," said Silas, "you're i' the right, Mrs. Win-

throp, you're i' the right.   There's good in this world —
I 've a feeling o' that now; and it makes a man feel as
there's a good more nor he can see, in spite o' the trouble
and the wickedness.   That drawing o' the lots is dark,
but the child was sent to me; there's dealings with us —   5
there's dealings."

This dialogue took place in Eppie's earlier years, when
Silas had to part with her for two hours every day, that
she might learn to read at the dame school, after he had
vainly tried himself to guide her in that first step to learn-   10
ing.   Now that she was grown up, Silas had often been
led, in those moments of quiet outpouring which come to
people who live together in perfect love, to talk with *her*,
too, of the past, and how and why he had lived a lonely
man until she had been sent to him.   For it would have   15
been impossible for him to hide from Eppie that she was
not his own child; even if the most delicate reticence on
the point could have been expected from Raveloe gos-
sips in her presence, her own questions about her mother
could not have been parried, as she grew up, without that   20
complete shrouding of the past which would have made a
painful barrier between their minds.   So Eppie had long
known how her mother had died on the snowy ground,
and how she herself had been found on the hearth by
father Silas, who had taken her golden curls for his lost   25
guineas brought back to him.   The tender and peculiar
love with which Silas had reared her in almost inseparable
companionship with himself, aided by the seclusion of their
dwelling, had preserved her from the lowering influences
of the village talk and habits, and had kept her mind in   30
that freshness which is sometimes falsely supposed to be
an invariable attribute of rusticity.   Perfect love has a
breath of poetry which can exalt the relations of the least-
instructed human beings, and this breath of poetry had

surrounded Eppie from the time when she had followed the bright gleam that beckoned her to Silas's hearth; so that it is not surprising if, in other things besides her delicate prettiness, she was not quite a common village maiden, but had a touch of refinement and fervor which came from no other teaching than that of tenderly nurtured, unvitiated feeling. She was too childish and simple for her imagination to rove into questions about her unknown father; for a long while it did not even occur to her that she must have had a father, and the first time that the idea of her mother having had a husband presented itself to her was when Silas showed her the wedding-ring which had been taken from the wasted finger, and had been carefully preserved by him in a little lacquered box shaped like a shoe. He delivered this box into Eppie's charge when she had grown up, and she often opened it to look at the ring; but still she thought hardly at all about the father of whom it was the symbol. Had she not a father very close to her, who loved her better than any real fathers in the village seemed to love their daughters? On the contrary, who her mother was and how she came to die in that forlornness were questions that often pressed on Eppie's mind. Her knowledge of Mrs. Winthrop, who was her nearest friend next to Silas, made her feel that a mother must be very precious; and she had again and again asked Silas to tell her how her mother looked, whom she was like, and how he had found her against the furze bush, led towards it by the little footsteps and the outstretched arms. The furze bush was there still; and this afternoon, when Eppie came out with Silas into the sunshine, it was the first object that arrested her eyes and thoughts.

"Father," she said, in a tone of gentle gravity, which sometimes came like a sadder, slower cadence across her playfulness, "we shall take the furze bush into the garden; it 'll come into the corner, and just against it I 'll put snow-drops and crocuses, 'cause Aaron says they won't die out, but 'll always get more and more."

"Ah, child," said Silas, always ready to talk when he had his pipe in his hand, apparently enjoying the pauses more than the puffs, "it would n't do to leave out the furze bush; and there 's nothing prettier, to my thinking, when it 's yellow with flowers. But it 's just come into my head what we 're to do for a fence — mayhap Aaron can help us to a thought; but a fence we must have, else the don-keys and things 'ull come and trample everything down. And fencing 's hard to be got at, by what I can make out."

"Oh, I 'll tell you, daddy," said Eppie, clasping her hands suddenly, after a minute's thought. "There 's lots o' loose stones about, some of 'em not big, and we might lay 'em atop of one another and make a wall. You and me could carry the smallest, and Aaron 'ud carry the rest — I know he would."

"Eh, my precious un," said Silas, "there is n't enough stones to go all round; and as for you carrying, why, wi' your little arms you could n't carry a stone no bigger than a turnip. You 're dillicate made, my dear," he added, with a tender intonation; "that 's what Mrs. Winthrop says."

"Oh, I 'm stronger than you think, daddy," said Eppie; "and if there was n't stones enough to go all round, why, they 'll go part o' the way, and then it 'll be easier to get sticks and things for the rest. See here, round the big pit, what a many stones!"

She skipped forward to the pit, meaning to lift one of the stones and exhibit her strength, but she started back in surprise.

"O father, just come and look here," she exclaimed;

"come and see how the water's gone down since yesterday.   Why, yesterday the pit was ever so full !"

"Well, to be sure," said Silas, coming to her side.
"Why, that's the draining they've begun on, since har-
5 vest, i' Mr. Osgood's fields, I reckon.   The foreman said
to me the other day, when I passed by 'em, 'Master Marner,' he said, 'I should n't wonder if we lay your bit o'
waste as dry as a bone.'   It was Mr. Godfrey Cass, he
said, had gone into the draining; he'd been taking these
10 fields o' Mr. Osgood."

"How odd it'll seem to have the old pit dried up!" said
Eppie, turning away and stooping to lift rather a large
stone.   "See, daddy, I can carry this quite well," she
said, going along with much energy for a few steps, but
15 presently letting it fall.

"Ah, you're fine and strong, aren't you?" said Silas,
while Eppie shook her aching arms and laughed.   "Come,
come, let us go and sit down on the bank against the stile
there, and have no more lifting.   You might hurt your-
20 self, child.   You'd need have somebody to work for you
— and my arm is n't over strong."

Silas uttered the last sentence slowly, as if it implied
more than met the ear ; and Eppie, when they sat down
on the bank, nestled close to his side, and, taking hold
25 caressingly of the arm that was not over strong, held it on
her lap, while Silas puffed again dutifully at the pipe, which
occupied his other arm.   An ash in the hedgerow behind
made a fretted screen from the sun, and threw happy,
playful shadows all about them.

30   "Father," said Eppie, very gently, after they had been
sitting in silence a little while, "if I was to be married,
ought I to be married with my mother's ring?"

Silas gave an almost imperceptible start, though the
question fell in with the undercurrent of thought in his

own mind, and then said, in a subdued tone, "Why, Eppie, have you been a-thinking on it?"

"Only this last week, father," said Eppie ingenuously, "since Aaron talked to me about it."

"And what did he say?" said Silas, still in the same subdued way, as if he were anxious lest he should fall into the slightest tone that was not for Eppie's good.

"He said he should like to be married, because he was a-going in four and twenty, and had got a deal of gardening work, now Mr. Mott's given up; and he goes twice a week regular to Mr. Cass's, and once to Mr. Osgood's, and they're going to take him on at the rectory."

"And who is it as he's wanting to marry?" said Silas, with rather a sad smile.

"Why, me, to be sure, daddy," said Eppie, with dimpling laughter, kissing her father's cheek; "as if he'd want to marry anybody else!"

"And you mean to have him, do you?" said Silas.

"Yes, some time," said Eppie; "I don't know when. Everybody's married some time, Aaron says. But I told him that wasn't true; for, I said, look at father — he's never been married."

"No, child," said Silas; "your father was a lone man till you was sent to him."

"But you'll never be lone again, father," said Eppie tenderly. "That was what Aaron said: 'I could never think o' taking you away from Master Marner, Eppie.' And I said, 'It 'ud be no use if you did, Aaron.' And he wants us all to live together, so as you needn't work a bit, father, only what's for your own pleasure; and he'd be as good as a son to you — that was what he said."

"And should you like that, Eppie?" said Silas, looking at her.

"I shouldn't mind it, father," said Eppie, quite simply.

"And I should like things to be so as you need n't work
much.   But if it was n't for that, I 'd sooner things did n't
change.   I 'm very happy; I like Aaron to be fond of me
and come and see us often and behave pretty to you —
5 he always *does* behave pretty to you, does n't he, father?"

"Yes, child; nobody could behave better," said Silas
emphatically.   "He 's his mother's lad."

"But I don't want any change," said Eppie.   "I should
like to go on a long, long while just as we are.   Only
10 Aaron does want a change; and he made me cry a bit —
only a bit — because he said I did n't care for him, for if
I cared for him I should want us to be married, as he did."

"Eh, my blessed child," said Silas, laying down his
pipe as if it were useless to pretend to smoke any longer,
15 "you 're o'er young to be married.   We 'll ask Mrs.
Winthrop — we 'll ask Aaron's mother what *she* thinks; if
there 's a right thing to do, she 'll come at it.   But there 's
this to be thought on, Eppie: things *will* change, whether
we like it or no; things won't go on for a long while just
20 as they are and no difference.   I shall get older and
helplesser, and be a burden on you, belike, if I don't go
away from you altogether.   Not as I mean you 'd think
me a burden — I know you would n't — but it 'ud be hard
upon you; and when I look for'ard to that I like to
25 think as you 'd have somebody else besides me — somebody young and strong, as 'll outlast your own life, and
take care on you to the end."   Silas paused, and, resting
his wrists on his knees, lifted his hands up and down
meditatively as he looked on the ground.

30   "Then would you like me to be married, father?" said
Eppie, with a little trembling in her voice.

"I 'll not be the man to say no, Eppie," said Silas emphatically; "but we 'll ask your godmother.   She 'll wish
the right thing by you and her son, too."

" There they come then," said Eppie. " Let us go and meet 'em. Oh, the pipe ! won't you have it lit again, father ? " said Eppie, lifting that medicinal appliance from the ground.

" Nay, child," said Silas ; " I 've done enough for to- 5 day. I think, mayhap, a little of it does me more good than so much at once."

CHAPTER XVII.

WHILE Silas and Eppie were seated on the bank
discoursing in the fleckered shade of the ash tree Miss
Priscilla Lammeter was resisting her sister's arguments
that it would be better to take tea at the Red House, and
5 let her father have a long nap, than drive home to the
Warrens so soon after dinner. The family party (of four
only) were seated round the table in the dark wainscoted
parlor, with the Sunday dessert before them, of fresh
filberts, apples, and pears, duly ornamented with leaves
10 by Nancy's own hand before the bells had rung for
church.

A great change has come over the dark wainscoted parlor since we saw it in Godfrey's bachelor days and under
the wifeless reign of the old Squire. Now all is polish,
15 on which no yesterday's dust is ever allowed to rest, from
the yard's width of oaken boards round the carpet to the
old Squire's gun and whips and walking-sticks, ranged on
the stag's antlers above the mantelpiece. All other signs
of sporting and outdoor occupation Nancy has removed
20 to another room; but she has brought into the Red House
the habit of filial reverence, and preserves sacredly in a
place of honor these relics of her husband's departed
father. The tankards are on the side-table still, but the
bossed silver is undimmed by handling, and there are no
25 dregs to send forth unpleasant suggestions; the only pre-
vailing scent is of the lavender and rose leaves that fill
the vases of Derbyshire spar. All is purity and order in
this once dreary room, for fifteen years ago it was entered
by a new presiding spirit.

"Now, father," said Nancy, "*is* there any call for you to go home to tea? May n't you just as well stay with us? — such a beautiful evening as it's likely to be."

The old gentleman had been talking with Godfrey about the increasing poor rate and the ruinous times, and had not heard the dialogue between his daughters.

"My dear, you must ask Priscilla," he said, in the once firm voice, now become rather broken. "She manages me and the farm, too."

"And reason good as I should manage you, father," said Priscilla, "else you'd be giving yourself your death with rheumatism. And as for the farm, if anything turns out wrong, as it can't but do in these times, there's nothing kills a man so soon as having nobody to find fault with but himself. It's a deal the best way o' being master to let somebody else do the ordering, and keep the blaming in your own hands. It 'ud save many a man a stroke, *I* believe."

"Well, well, my dear," said her father, with a quiet laugh, "I didn't say you don't manage for everybody's good."

"Then manage so as you may stay tea, Priscilla," said Nancy, putting her hand on her sister's arm affectionately. "Come now; and we'll go round the garden while father has his nap."

"My dear child, he'll have a beautiful nap in the gig, for I shall drive. And as for staying tea, I can't hear of it; for there's this dairymaid, now she knows she's to be married turned Michaelmas, she'd as lief pour the new milk into the pig-trough as into the pans. That's the way with 'em all; it's as if they thought the world 'ud be new made because they're to be married. So come and let me put my bonnet on, and there'll be time for us to walk round the garden while the horse is being put in."

When the sisters were treading the neatly swept garden walks, between the bright turf that contrasted pleasantly with the dark cones and arches and wall-like hedges of yew, Priscilla said :

5 "I'm as glad as anything at your husband's making that exchange o' land with Cousin Osgood, and beginning the dairying. It's a thousand pities you didn't do it before; for it'll give you something to fill your mind. There's nothing like a dairy if folks want a bit o' worrit 10 to make the days pass. For as for rubbing furniture, when you can once see your face in a table there's nothing else to look for; but there's always something fresh with the dairy; for even in the depths o' winter there's some pleasure in conquering the butter, and making it 15 come, whether or no. My dear," added Priscilla, pressing her sister's hand affectionately as they walked side by side, "you'll never be low when you've got a dairy."

"Ah, Priscilla," said Nancy, returning the pressure with a grateful glance of her clear eyes, "but it won't 20 make up to Godfrey; a dairy's not so much to a man. And it's only what he cares for that ever makes me low. I'm contented with the blessings we have, if he could be contented."

"It drives me past patience," said Priscilla impetuously, 25 "that way o' the men — always wanting and wanting, and never easy with what they've got; they can't sit comfortable in their chairs when they've neither ache nor pain, but either they must stick a pipe in their mouths, to make 'em better than well, or else they must be swallowing 30 something strong, though they're forced to make haste before the next meal comes in. But, joyful be it spoken, our father was never that sort o' man. And if it had pleased God to make you ugly, like me, so as the men wouldn't ha' run after you, we might have kept to our own family, and had nothing to do with folks as have got uneasy blood in their veins."

"Oh, don't say so, Priscilla," said Nancy, repenting that she had called forth this outburst; "nobody has any occasion to find fault with Godfrey. It's natural he should be disappointed at not having any children; every man likes to have somebody to work for and lay by for, and he always counted so on making a fuss with 'em when they were little. There's many another man 'ud hanker more than he does. He's the best of husbands."

"Oh, I know," said Priscilla, smiling sarcastically. "I know the way o' wives; they set one on to abuse their husbands, and then they turn round on one and praise 'em as if they wanted to sell 'em. But father 'll be waiting for me; we must turn now."

The large gig with the steady old gray was at the front door, and Mr. Lammeter was already on the stone steps, passing the time in recalling to Godfrey what very fine points Speckle had when his master used to ride him.

"I always *would* have a good horse, you know," said the old gentleman, not liking that spirited time to be quite effaced from the memory of his juniors.

"Mind you bring Nancy to the Warrens before the week's out, Mr. Cass," was Priscilla's parting injunction, as she took the reins and shook them gently, by way of friendly incitement to Speckle.

"I shall just take a turn to the fields against the Stone-pits, Nancy, and look at the draining," said Godfrey.

"You'll be in again by tea time, dear?"

"Oh, yes; I shall be back in an hour."

It was Godfrey's custom on a Sunday afternoon to do a little contemplative farming in a leisurely walk. Nancy seldom accompanied him; for the women of her generation — unless, like Priscilla, they took to outdoor manage-

ment — were not given to much walking beyond their
own house and garden, finding sufficient exercise in
domestic duties. So, when Priscilla was not with her,
she usually sat with Mant's Bible before her, and, after
5 following the text with her eyes for a little while, she
would gradually permit them to wander as her thoughts
had already insisted on wandering.

But Nancy's Sunday thoughts were rarely quite out of
keeping with the devout and reverential intention implied
10 by the book spread open before her. She was not theo-
logically instructed enough to discern very clearly the relation between the sacred documents of the past which
she opened without method and her own obscure, simple
life ; but the spirit of rectitude and the sense of responsi-
15 bility for the effect of her conduct on others, which were
strong elements in Nancy's character, had made it a habit
with her to scrutinize her past feelings and actions with
self-questioning solicitude. Her mind not being courted
by a great variety of subjects, she filled the vacant
20 moments by living inwardly, again and again, through all
her remembered experience, especially through the fifteen
years of her married time, in which her life and its
significance had been doubled. She recalled the small
details, the words, tones, and looks, in the critical scenes
25 which had opened a new epoch for her by giving her a
deeper insight into the relations and trials of life, or which
had called on her for some little effort of forbearance or
of painful adherence to an imagined or real duty — asking
herself continually whether she had been in any respect
30 blamable. This excessive rumination and self-questioning
is perhaps a morbid habit inevitable to a mind of much
moral sensibility when shut out from its due share of
outward activity and of practical claims on its affections
— inevitable to a noble-hearted, childless woman when

her lot is narrow. "I can do so little — have I done it all well?" is the perpetually recurring thought; and there are no voices calling her away from that soliloquy, no peremptory demands to divert energy from vain regret or superfluous scruple.

There was one main thread of painful experience in Nancy's married life, and on it hung certain deeply felt scenes, which were the oftenest revived in retrospect. The short dialogue with Priscilla in the garden had determined the current of retrospect in that frequent direction this particular Sunday afternoon. The first wandering of her thought from the text, which she still attempted dutifully to follow with her eyes and silent lips, was into an imaginary enlargement of the defense she had set up for her husband against Priscilla's implied blame. The vindication of the loved object is the best balm affection can find for its wounds. "A man must have so much on his mind" is the belief by which a wife often supports a cheerful face under rough answers and unfeeling words. And Nancy's deepest wounds had all come from the perception that the absence of children from their hearth was dwelt on in her husband's mind as a privation to which he could not reconcile himself.

Yet sweet Nancy might have been expected to feel still more keenly the denial of a blessing to which she had looked forward with all the varied expectations and preparations, solemn and prettily trivial, which fill the mind of a loving woman when she expects to become a mother. Was there not a drawer filled with the neat work of her hands, all unworn and untouched, just as she had arranged it there fourteen years ago — just, but for one little dress, which had been made the burial dress? But under this immediate personal trial Nancy was so firmly unmurmuring that years ago she had suddenly renounced the habit of visiting this drawer, lest she should in this way be cherishing a longing for what was not given.

Perhaps it was this very severity towards any indulgence of what she held to be sinful regret in herself that made her shrink from applying her own standard to her husband. " It is very different — it is much worse for a man to be disappointed in that way; a woman can always be satisfied with devoting herself to her husband, but a man wants something that will make him look forward more, and sitting by the fire is so much duller to him than to a woman." And always when Nancy reached this point in her meditations — trying, with predetermined sympathy, to see everything as Godfrey saw it — there came a renewal of self-questioning. *Had* she done everything in her power to lighten Godfrey's privation ? Had she really been right in the resistance which had cost her so much pain six years ago and again four years ago,— the resistance to her husband's wish that they should adopt a child ? Adoption was more remote from the ideas and habits of that time than of our own ; still, Nancy had her opinion on it. It was as necessary to her mind to have an opinion on all topics, not exclusively masculine, that had come under her notice as for her to have a precisely marked place for every article of her personal property; and her opinions were always principles to be unwaveringly acted on. They were firm, not because of their basis, but because she held them with a tenacity inseparable from her mental action. On all the duties and proprieties of life, from filial behavior to the arrangements of the evening toilet, pretty Nancy Lammeter, by the time she was three and twenty, had her unalterable little code, and had formed every one of her habits in strict accordance with that code. She carried these decided judgments within her in the most unobtrusive way ; they rooted themselves in her mind and

grew there as quietly as grass.   Years ago, we know, she
insisted on dressing like Priscilla, because "it was right
for sisters to dress alike," and because "she would do what
was right if she wore a gown dyed with cheese coloring."
That was a trivial but typical instance of the mode in which   5
Nancy's life was regulated.

It was one of those rigid principles, and no petty egois-
tic feeling, which had been the ground of Nancy's difficult
resistance to her husband's wish.   To adopt a child, because children of your own had been denied you, was to try   10
and choose your lot in spite of Providence ; the adopted
child, she was convinced, would never turn out well, and
would be a curse to those who had willfully and rebelliously
sought what it was clear that, for some high reason, they
were better without.   When you saw a thing was not meant   15
to be, said Nancy, it was a bounden duty to leave off so
much as wishing for it.   And so far, perhaps, the wisest
of men could scarcely make more than a verbal improve-
ment in her principle.   But the conditions under which
she held it apparent that a thing was not meant to be de-   20
pended on a more peculiar mode of thinking.   She would
have given up making a purchase at a particular place if,
on three successive times, rain or some other cause of
Heaven's sending had formed an obstacle ; and she would
have anticipated a broken limb or other heavy misfortune   25
to any one who persisted in spite of such indications.

"But why should you think the child would turn out
ill?" said Godfrey, in his remonstrances.   "She has thriven
as well as child can do with the weaver ; and *he* adopted
her.   There is n't such a pretty little girl anywhere else   30
in the parish, or one fitter for the station we could give
her.   Where can be the likelihood of her being a curse to
anybody?"

"Yes, my dear Godfrey," said Nancy, who was sitting

with her hands tightly clasped together and with yearning, regretful affection in her eyes. " The child may not turn out ill with the weaver. But, then, he did n't go to seek her, as we should be doing. It will be wrong ; I feel
5 sure it will. Don't you remember what that lady we met at the Royston Baths told us about the child her sister adopted ? That was the only adopting I ever heard of ; and the child was transported when it was twenty-three. Dear Godfrey, don't ask me to do what I know is wrong ;
10 I should never be happy again. I know it 's very hard for *you* — it 's easier for me — but it 's the will of Providence."

It might seem singular that Nancy — with her religious theory pieced together out of narrow social traditions,
15 fragments of church doctrine imperfectly understood, and girlish reasonings on her small experience — should have arrived by herself at a way of thinking so nearly akin to that of many devout people whose beliefs are held in the shape of a system quite remote from her knowledge — sin-
20 gular, if we did not know that human beliefs, like all other natural growths, elude the barriers of system.

Godfrey had from the first specified Eppie, then about twelve years old, as a child suitable for them to adopt. It had never occurred to him that Silas would rather part
25 with his life than with Eppie. Surely the weaver would wish the best to the child he had taken so much trouble with and would be glad that such good fortune should happen to her; she would always be very grateful to him, and he would be well provided for to the end of his life—
30 provided for as the excellent part he had done by the child deserved. Was it not an appropriate thing for people in a higher station to take a charge off the hands of a man in a lower ? It seemed an eminently appropriate thing to Godfrey, for reasons that were known only to himself ;

and by a common fallacy he imagined the measure would
be easy because he had private motives for desiring it.
This was rather a coarse mode of estimating Silas's relation
to Eppie; but we must remember that many of the impressions which Godfrey was likely to gather concerning the 5
laboring people around him would favor the idea that
deep affections can hardly go along with callous palms and
scant means ; and he had not had the opportunity, even if
he had had the power, of entering intimately into all that
was exceptional in the weaver's experience. It was only 10
the want of adequate knowledge that could have made it
possible for Godfrey deliberately to entertain an unfeeling
project; his natural kindness had outlived that blighting
time of cruel wishes, and Nancy's praise of him as a husband was not founded entirely on a willful illusion. 15

" I was right," she said to herself, when she had recalled
all their scenes of discussion ; " I feel I was right to say
him nay, though it hurt me more than anything. But how
good Godfrey has been about it ! Many men would have
been very angry with me for standing out against their 20
wishes, and they might have thrown out that they 'd had
ill luck in marrying me ; but Godfrey has never been the
man to say me an unkind word. It 's only what he can't
hide; everything seems so blank to him, I know. And the
land — what a difference it 'ud make to him, when he goes 25
to see after things, if he 'd children growing up that he was
doing it all for ! But I won't murmur ; and perhaps if
he 'd married a woman who 'd have had children she 'd
have vexed him in other ways."

This possibility was Nancy's chief comfort ; and to give 30
it greater strength she labored to make it impossible that
any other wife should have had more perfect tenderness.
She had been *forced* to vex him by that one denial. Godfrey was not insensible to her loving effort, and did Nancy

no injustice as to the motives of her obstinacy. It was
impossible to have lived with her fifteen years and not be
aware that an unselfish clinging to the right and a sincerity clear as the flower-born dew were her main charac-
5 teristics; indeed, Godfrey felt this so strongly that his
own more wavering nature, too averse to facing difficulty
to be unvaryingly simple and truthful, was kept in a certain awe of this gentle wife who watched his looks with a
yearning to obey them. It seemed to him impossible that he
10 should ever confess to her the truth about Eppie; she would
never recover from the repulsion the story of his earlier
marriage would create, told to her now, after that long concealment. And the child, too, he thought, must become
an object of repulsion; the very sight of her would be
15 painful. The shock to Nancy's mingled pride and ignorance of the world's evil might even be too much for her
delicate frame. Since he had married her with that secret
on his heart, he must keep it there to the last. Whatever
else he did, he could not make an irreparable breach be-
20 tween himself and this long-loved wife.

Meanwhile, why could he not make up his mind to the
absence of children from a hearth brightened by such a
wife? Why did his mind fly uneasily to that void, as if it
were the sole reason why life was not thoroughly joyous to
25 him? I suppose it is the way with all men and women who
reach middle age without the clear perception that life never
can be thoroughly joyous; under the vague dullness of the
gray hours, dissatisfaction seeks a definite object, and finds
it in the privation of an untried good. Dissatisfaction
30 seated musingly on a childless hearth thinks with envy of
the father whose return is greeted by young voices; seated
at the meal where the little heads rise one above another
like nursery plants, it sees a black care hovering behind
every one of them, and thinks the impulses by which men

abandon freedom and seek for ties are surely nothing but a brief madness. In Godfrey's case there were further reasons why his thoughts should be continually solicited by this one point in his lot: his conscience, never thoroughly easy about Eppie, now gave his childless home the aspect of a retribution; and as the time passed on, under Nancy's refusal to adopt her, any retrieval of his error became more and more difficult.

On this Sunday afternoon it was already four years since there had been any allusion to the subject between them, and Nancy supposed that it was forever buried.

"I wonder if he 'll mind it less or more as he gets older," she thought. "I 'm afraid more. Aged people feel the miss of children; what would father do without Priscilla? And if I die Godfrey will be very lonely — not holding together with his brothers much. But I won't be over anxious, and trying to make things out beforehand; I must do my best for the present."

With that last thought Nancy roused herself from her reverie and turned her eyes again towards the forsaken page. It had been forsaken longer than she imagined, for she was presently surprised by the appearance of the servant with the tea things. It was, in fact, a little before the usual time for tea; but Jane had her reasons.

"Is your master come into the yard, Jane?"

"No, 'm, he is n't," said Jane, with a slight emphasis, of which, however, her mistress took no notice.

"I don't know whether you 've seen 'em, 'm," continued Jane, after a pause, "but there 's folks making haste all one way, afore the front window. I doubt something 's happened. There 's niver a man to be seen i' the yard, else I 'd send and see. I 've been up into the top attic, but there 's no seeing anything for trees. I hope nobody 's hurt, that 's all."

"Oh, no, I daresay there's nothing much the matter," said Nancy. "It's perhaps Mr. Snell's bull got out again, as he did before."

"I wish he may n't gore anybody then, that's all," said Jane, not altogether despising a hypothesis which covered a few imaginary calamities.

"That girl is always terrifying me," thought Nancy. "I wish Godfrey would come in."

She went to the front window and looked as far as she could see along the road, with an uneasiness which she felt to be childish, for there were now no such signs of excitement as Jane had spoken of, and Godfrey would not be likely to return by the village road, but by the fields. She continued to stand, however, looking at the placid churchyard with the long shadows of the grave-stones across the bright green hillocks, and at the glowing autumn colors of the rectory trees beyond. Before such calm external beauty the presence of a vague fear is more distinctly felt, — like a raven flapping its slow wing across the sunny air. Nancy wished more and more that Godfrey would come in.

CHAPTER XVIII.

SOME one opened the door at the other end of the room, and Nancy felt that it was her husband. She turned from the window with gladness in her eyes, for the wife's chief dread was stilled.

"Dear, I 'm so thankful you 're come," she said, going towards him. "I began to get—"

She paused abruptly, for Godfrey was laying down his hat with trembling hands, and turned towards her with a pale face and a strange, unanswering glance, as if he saw her indeed, but saw her as part of a scene invisible to herself. She laid her hand on his arm, not daring to speak again ; but he left the touch unnoticed, and threw himself into his chair.

Jane was already at the door with the hissing urn. "Tell her to keep away, will you ?" said Godfrey ; and when the door was closed again he exerted himself to speak more distinctly.

"Sit down, Nancy — there," he said, pointing to a chair opposite him. "I came back as soon as I could, to hinder anybody's telling you but me. I 've had a great shock ; but I care most about the shock it 'll be to you."

"It is n't father and Priscilla ?" said Nancy, with quivering lips, clasping her hands together tightly on her lap.

"No, it 's nobody living," said Godfrey, unequal to the considerate skill with which he would have wished to make his revelation. "It 's Dunstan, — my brother Dunstan, that we lost sight of sixteen years ago. We 've found him — found his body — his skeleton."

The deep dread Godfrey's look had created in Nancy made her feel these words a relief. She sat in comparative calmness to hear what else he had to tell. He went on :

5　　"The Stone-pit has gone dry suddenly — from the draining, I suppose; and there he lies — has lain for sixteen years, wedged between two great stones. There's his watch and seals, and there's my gold-handled hunting whip, with my name on; he took it away, without my knowing, the day he went hunting on Wild-fire, the last time he was seen."

Godfrey paused; it was not so easy to say what came next. "Do you think he drowned himself?" said Nancy, almost wondering that her husband should be so deeply shaken by what had happened all those years ago to an unloved brother, of whom worse things had been augured.

"No, he fell in," said Godfrey, in a low but distinct voice, as if he felt some deep meaning in the fact. Presently he added : "Dunstan was the man that robbed Silas Marner."

The blood rushed to Nancy's face and neck at this surprise and shame, for she had been bred up to regard even a distant kinship with crime as a dishonor.

"O Godfrey!" she said, with compassion in her tone, for she had immediately reflected that the dishonor must be felt still more keenly by her husband.

"There was the money in the pit," he continued, "all the weaver's money. Everything's been gathered up, and they're taking the skeleton to the Rainbow. But I came back to tell you; there was no hindering it — you must know."

He was silent, looking on the ground for two long minutes. Nancy would have said some words of comfort under this disgrace, but she refrained, from an instinctive

sense that there was something behind — that Godfrey
had something else to tell her.   Presently he lifted his
eyes to her face and kept them fixed on her, as he
said :

"Everything comes to light, Nancy, sooner or later.   5
When God Almighty wills it our secrets are found out.
I 've lived with a secret on my mind, but I 'll keep it from
you no longer.   I would n't have you know it by somebody else, and not by me.   I would n't have you find it
out after I 'm dead.   I 'll tell you now.   It 's been 'I   10
will' and 'I won't' with me all my life.   I 'll make sure
of myself now."

Nancy's utmost dread had returned.   The eyes of the
husband and wife met with awe in them, as at a crisis
which suspended affection.   15

"Nancy," said Godfrey slowly, "when I married you, I
hid something from you — something I ought to have
told you.   That woman Marner found dead in the snow —
Eppie's mother — that wretched woman — was my wife ;
Eppie is my child."   20

He paused, dreading the effect of his confession.   But
Nancy sat quite still, only that her eyes dropped and
ceased to meet his.   She was pale and quiet as a medita-
tive statue, clasping her hands on her lap.

"You 'll never think the same of me again," said God-   25
frey, after a little while, with some tremor in his voice.

She was silent.

"I ought n't to have left the child unowned ; I ought n't
to have kept it from you.   But I could n't bear to give
you up, Nancy.   I was led away into marrying her — I   30
suffered for it."

Still Nancy was silent, looking down ; and he almost
expected that she would presently get up and say she
would go to her father's.   How could she have any mercy

for faults that must seem so black to her, with her simple, severe notions?

But at last she lifted up her eyes to his again and spoke. There was no indignation in her voice — only
5 deep regret.

"Godfrey, if you had but told me this six years ago, we could have done some of our duty by the child. Do you think I'd have refused to take her in if I'd known she was yours?"

10   At that moment Godfrey felt all the bitterness of an error that was not simply futile, but had defeated its own end. He had not measured this wife with whom he had lived so long. But she spoke again, with more agitation.

"And — O Godfrey — if we'd had her from the first,
15 if you'd taken to her as you ought, she'd have loved me for her mother — and you'd have been happier with me. I could better have bore my little baby dying, and our life might have been more like what we used to think it 'ud be."

20   The tears fell, and Nancy ceased to speak.

"But you wouldn't have married me then, Nancy, if I'd told you," said Godfrey, urged, in the bitterness of his self-reproach, to prove to himself that his conduct had not been utter folly. "You may think you would now,
25 but you wouldn't then. With your pride and your father's, you'd have hated having anything to do with me after the talk there'd have been."

"I can't say what I should have done about that, Godfrey. I should never have married anybody else.
30 But I wasn't worth doing wrong for; nothing is in this world. Nothing is so good as it seems beforehand; not even our marrying wasn't, you see." There was a faint, sad smile on Nancy's face as she said the last words.

"I'm a worse man than you thought I was, Nancy,"

said Godfrey, rather tremulously. "Can you forgive me ever?"

"The wrong to me is but little, Godfrey; you've made it up to me — you've been good to me for fifteen years. It's another you did the wrong to; and I doubt it can 5 never be all made up for."

"But we can take Eppie now," said Godfrey. "I won't mind the world knowing at last. I'll be plain and open for the rest o' my life."

"It'll be different coming to us now she's grown up," 10 said Nancy, shaking her head sadly. "But it's your duty to acknowledge her and provide for her; and I'll do my part by her and pray to God Almighty to make her love me."

"Then we'll go together to Silas Marner's this very 15 night, as soon as everything's quiet at the Stone-pits."

CHAPTER XIX.

BETWEEN eight and nine o'clock that evening Eppie and Silas were seated alone in the cottage. After the great excitement the weaver had undergone from the events of the afternoon, he had felt a longing for this quietude, 5 and had even begged Mrs. Winthrop and Aaron, who had naturally lingered behind every one else, to leave him alone with his child. The excitement had not passed away; it had only reached that stage when the keenness of the susceptibility makes external stimulus intolerable 10 — when there is no sense of weariness, but rather an intensity of inward life, under which sleep is an impossibility. Any one who has watched such moments in other men remembers the brightness of the eyes and the strange definiteness that comes over coarse features from that 15 transient influence. It is as if a new fineness of ear for all spiritual voices had sent wonder-working vibrations through the heavy mortal frame — as if "beauty born of murmuring sound" had passed into the face of the listener.

20 Silas's face showed that sort of transfiguration, as he sat in his armchair and looked at Eppie. She had drawn her own chair towards his knees, and leaned forward, holding both his hands, while she looked up at him. On the table near them, lit by a candle, lay the recovered 25 gold, — the old long-loved gold, ranged in orderly heaps, as Silas used to range it in the days when it was his only joy. He had been telling her how he used to count it every night, and how his soul was utterly desolate till she was sent to him.

"At first I'd a sort o' feeling come across me now and then," he was saying in a subdued tone, "as if you might be changed into the gold again; for sometimes, turn my head which way I would, I seemed to see the gold, and I thought I should be glad if I could feel it and find it was come back. But that did n't last long. After a bit, I should have thought it was a curse come again, if it had drove you from me, for I 'd got to feel the need o' your looks and your voice and the touch o' your little fingers. You did n't know then, Eppie, when you were such a little un — you did n't know what your old father Silas felt for you."

"But I know now, father," said Eppie. "If it had n't been for you, they 'd have taken me to the workhouse, and there 'd have been nobody to love me."

"Eh, my precious child, the blessing was mine. If you had n't been sent to save me, I should ha' gone to the grave in my misery. The money was taken away from me in time; and you see it 's been kept — kept till it was wanted for you. It 's wonderful — our life is wonderful."

Silas sat in silence a few minutes, looking at the money. "It takes no hold of me now," he said ponderingly, "the money does n't. I wonder if it ever could again; I doubt it might if I lost you, Eppie. I might come to think I was forsaken again and lose the feeling that God was good to me."

At that moment there was a knocking at the door, and Eppie was obliged to rise without answering Silas. Beautiful she looked, with the tenderness of gathering tears in her eyes and a slight flush on her cheeks, as she stepped to open the door. The flush deepened when she saw Mr. and Mrs. Godfrey Cass. She made her little rustic curtsy, and held the door wide for them to enter.

"We 're disturbing you very late, my dear," said Mrs.

Cass, taking Eppie's hand and looking in her face with an expression of anxious interest and admiration. Nancy herself was pale and tremulous.

Eppie, after placing chairs for Mr. and Mrs. Cass, went to stand against Silas, opposite to them.

"Well, Marner," said Godfrey, trying to speak with perfect firmness, "it's a great comfort to me to see you with your money again, that you've been deprived of so many years. It was one of my family did you the wrong — the more grief to me — and I feel bound to make up to you for it in every way. Whatever I can do for you will be nothing but paying a debt, even if I looked no further than the robbery. But there are other things I'm beholden — shall be beholden to you for, Marner."

Godfrey checked himself. It had been agreed between him and his wife that the subject of his fatherhood should be approached very carefully, and that, if possible, the disclosure should be reserved for the future, so that it might be made to Eppie gradually. Nancy had urged this, because she felt strongly the painful light in which Eppie must inevitably see the relation between her father and mother.

Silas, always ill at ease when he was being spoken to by "betters," such as Mr. Cass, — tall, powerful, florid men, seen chiefly on horseback, — answered with some constraint :

"Sir, I've a deal to thank you for a'ready. As for the robbery, I count it no loss to me. And if I did, you couldn't help it ; you aren't answerable for it."

"You may look at it in that way, Marner, but I never can ; and I hope you'll let me act according to my own feeling of what's just. I know you're easily contented ; you've been a hard-working man all your life."

"Yes, sir, yes," said Marner meditatively. "I should

ha' been bad off without my work; it was what I held by when everything else was gone from me."

"Ah," said Godfrey, applying Marner's words simply to his bodily wants, "it was a good trade for you in this country, because there's been a great deal of linen 5 weaving to be done. But you're getting rather past such close work, Marner; it's time you laid by and had some rest. You look a good deal pulled down, though you're not an old man, *are* you?"

"Fifty-five, as near as I can say, sir," said Silas. 10

"Oh, why, you may live thirty years longer — look at old Macey! And that money on the table, after all, is but little. It won't go far either way — whether it's put out to interest or you were to live on it as long as it would last; it would n't go far if you'd nobody to keep but 15 yourself, and you've had two to keep for a good many years now."

"Eh, sir," said Silas, unaffected by anything Godfrey was saying, "I'm in no fear o' want. We shall do very well — Eppie and me 'ull do well enough. There's few 20 working folks have got so much laid by as that. I don't know what it is to gentlefolks, but I look upon it as a deal — almost too much. And, as for us, it's little we want."

"Only the garden, father," said Eppie, blushing up to 25 the ears the moment after.

"You love a garden, do you, my dear?" said Nancy, thinking that this turn in the point of view might help her husband. "We should agree in that; I give a deal of time to the garden." 30

"Ah, there's plenty of gardening at the Red House," said Godfrey, surprised at the difficulty he found in approaching a proposition which had seemed so easy to him in the distance. "You've done a good part by

Eppie, Marner, for sixteen years. It 'ud be a great comfort to you to see her well provided for, would n't it? She
looks blooming and healthy, but not fit for any hardships ;
she does n't look like a strapping girl come of working
5 parents. You 'd like to see her taken care of by those
who can leave her well off and make a lady of her ; she 's
more fit for it than for a rough life, such as she might
come to have in a few years' time."

A slight flush came over Marner's face and disappeared,
10 like a passing gleam. Eppie was simply wondering Mr.
Cass should talk so about things that seemed to have
nothing to do with reality, but Silas was hurt and
uneasy.

"I don't take your meaning, sir," he answered, not
15 having words at command to express the mingled feelings
with which he had heard Mr. Cass's words.

"Well, my meaning is this, Marner," said Godfrey,
determined to come to the point. "Mrs. Cass and I, you
know, have no children — nobody to be the better for our
20 good home and everything else we have — more than
enough for ourselves. And we should like to have
somebody in the place of a daughter to us — we should
like to have Eppie, and treat her in every way as our own
child. It 'ud be a great comfort to you in your old age,
25 I hope, to see her fortune made in that way, after you 've
been at the trouble of bringing her up so well. And it 's
right you should have every reward for that. And Eppie,
I 'm sure, will always love you and be grateful to you ;
she 'd come and see you very often, and we should all be
30 on the lookout to do everything we could towards making
you comfortable."

A plain man like Godfrey Cass, speaking under some
embarrassment, necessarily blunders on words that are
coarser than his intentions, and that are likely to fall

gratingly on susceptible feelings. While he had been speaking Eppie had quietly passed her arm behind Silas's head and let her hand rest against it caressingly ; she felt him trembling violently. He was silent for some moments when Mr. Cass had ended, powerless under the conflict of emotions, all alike painful. Eppie's heart was swelling at the sense that her father was in distress ; and she was just going to lean down and speak to him when one struggling dread at last gained the mastery over every other in Silas, and he said faintly :

"Eppie, my child, speak. I won't stand in your way. Thank Mr. and Mrs. Cass."

Eppie took her hand from her father's head and came forward a step. Her cheeks were flushed, but not with shyness this time ; the sense that her father was in doubt and suffering banished that sort of self-consciousness. She dropped a low curtsy, first to Mrs. Cass and then to Mr. Cass, and said :

"Thank you, ma'am — thank you, sir. But I can't leave my father, nor own anybody nearer than him. And I don't want to be a lady — thank you all the same" (here Eppie dropped another curtsy). "I couldn't give up the folks I've been used to."

Eppie's lip began to tremble a little at the last words. She retreated to her father's chair again and held him round the neck, while Silas, with a subdued sob, put up his hand to grasp hers.

The tears were in Nancy's eyes, but her sympathy with Eppie was, naturally, divided with distress on her husband's account. She dared not speak, wondering what was going on in her husband's mind.

Godfrey felt an irritation inevitable to almost all of us when we encounter an unexpected obstacle. He had been full of his own penitence and resolution to retrieve his

error as far as the time was left to him ; he was possessed
with all-important feelings that were to lead to a predetermined course of action which he had fixed on as the
right, and he was not prepared to enter with lively
5 appreciation into other people's feelings counteracting his
virtuous resolves. The agitation with which he spoke
again was not quite unmixed with anger.

" But I 've a claim on you, Eppie, — the strongest of all
claims.   It 's my duty, Marner, to own Eppie as my child
10 and provide for her.   She 's my own child ; her mother
was my wife.   I 've a natural claim on her that must
stand before every other."

Eppie had given a violent start and turned quite pale.
Silas, on the contrary, who had been relieved by Eppie's
15 answer from the dread lest his mind should be in opposi-
tion to hers, felt the spirit of resistance in him set free,
not without a touch of parental fierceness.   " Then, sir,"
he answered, with an accent of bitterness that had been
silent in him since the memorable day when his youthful
20 hope had perished, " then, sir, why did n't you say so
sixteen year ago, and claim her before I 'd come to love
her, i'stead o' coming to take her from me now, when you
might as well take the heart out o' my body?   God gave
her to me because you turned your back upon her, and
25 He looks upon her as mine ; you 've no right to her !
When a man turns a blessing from his door it falls to
them as take it in."

" I know that, Marner.   I was wrong.   I 've repented
of my conduct in that matter," said Godfrey, who could
30 not help feeling the edge of Silas's words.

" I 'm glad to hear it, sir," said Marner, with gathering
excitement ; " but repentance does n't alter what 's been
going on for sixteen year.   Your coming now and saying ' I 'm her father ' does n't alter the feelings inside us.

It's me she's been calling her father ever since she could say the word."

"But I think you might look at the thing more reasonably, Marner," said Godfrey, unexpectedly awed by the weaver's direct truth speaking. "It isn't as if she was 5 to be taken quite away from you, so that you'd never see her again. She'll be very near you and come to see you very often. She'll feel just the same towards you."

"Just the same?" said Marner, more bitterly than ever. "How'll she feel just the same for me as she 10 does now, when we eat o' the same bit and drink o' the same cup and think o' the same things from one day's end to another? Just the same? That's idle talk. You'd cut us i' two."

Godfrey, unqualified by experience to discern the preg- 15 nancy of Marner's simple words, felt rather angry again. It seemed to him that the weaver was very selfish (a judgment readily passed by those who have never tested their own power of sacrifice) to oppose what was undoubtedly for Eppie's welfare; and he felt himself called upon, for 20 her sake, to assert his authority.

"I should have thought, Marner," he said severely, "I should have thought your affection for Eppie would make you rejoice in what was for her good, even if it did call upon you to give up something. You ought to remember 25 your own life's uncertain, and she's at an age now when her lot may soon be fixed in a way very different from what it would be in her father's home; she may marry some low workingman, and then, whatever I might do for her, I couldn't make her well off. You're putting your- 30 self in the way of her welfare; and, though I'm sorry to hurt you after what you've done and what I've left undone, I feel now it's my duty to insist on taking care of my own daughter. I want to do my duty."

It would be difficult to say whether it were Silas or
Eppie that was more deeply stirred by this last speech of
Godfrey's. Thought had been very busy in Eppie as she
listened to the contest between her old, long-loved father
5 and this new, unfamiliar father who had suddenly come to
fill the place of that black featureless shadow which had
held the ring and placed it on her mother's finger. Her
imagination had darted backward in conjectures and forward in previsions of what this revealed fatherhood
10 implied ; and there were words in Godfrey's last speech
which helped to make the previsions especially definite.
Not that these thoughts, either of past or future, determined her resolution—*that* was determined by the feelings
which vibrated to every word Silas had uttered ; but they
15 raised, even apart from these feelings, a repulsion towards
the offered lot and the newly revealed father.

Silas, on the other hand, was again stricken in conscience, and alarmed lest Godfrey's accusation should be
true — lest he should be raising his own will as an obstacle
20 to Eppie's good. For many moments he was mute,
struggling for the self-conquest necessary to the uttering
of the difficult words. They came out tremulously.

"I'll say no more. Let it be as you will. Speak to
the child. I'll hinder nothing."

25 Even Nancy, with all the acute sensibility of her own
affections, shared her husband's view, that Marner was
not justifiable in his wish to retain Eppie, after her real
father had avowed himself. She felt that it was a very
hard trial for the poor weaver, but her code allowed
30 no question that a father by blood must have a claim
above that of any foster father. Besides, Nancy, used all
her life to plenteous circumstances and the privileges of
"respectability," could not enter into the pleasures which
early nurture and habit connect with all the little aims

and efforts of the poor who are born poor; to her mind, Eppie, in being restored to her birthright, was entering on a too long withheld but unquestionable good. Hence she heard Silas's last words with relief, and thought, as Godfrey did, that their wish was achieved. 5

"Eppie, my dear," said Godfrey, looking at his daughter, not without some embarrassment, under the sense that she was old enough to judge him, "it'll always be our wish that you should show your love and gratitude to one who's been a father to you so many years, and we 10 shall want to help you to make him comfortable in every way. But we hope you'll come to love us as well; and, though I haven't been what a father should ha' been to you all these years, I wish to do the utmost in my power for you for the rest of my life and provide for you as my 15 only child. And you'll have the best of mothers in my wife; that'll be a blessing you haven't known since you were old enough to know it.

"My dear, you'll be a treasure to me," said Nancy, in her gentle voice. "We shall want for nothing when we 20 have our daughter."

Eppie did not come forward and curtsy, as she had done before. She held Silas's hand in hers and grasped it firmly — it was a weaver's hand, with a palm and finger tips that were sensitive to such pressure — while she 25 spoke with colder decision than before.

"Thank you, ma'am — thank you, sir, for your offers; they're very great and far above my wish. For I should have no delight i' life any more if I was forced to go away from my father and knew he was sitting at home, 30 a-thinking of me and feeling lone. We've been used to be happy together every day, and I can't think o' no happiness without him. And he says he'd nobody i' the world till I was sent to him, and he'd have nothing when I was

gone. And he 's took care of me and loved me from the
first, and I 'll cleave to him as long as he lives, and
nobody shall ever come between him and me."

" But you must make sure, Eppie," said Silas, in a low
5 voice, " you must make sure as you won't ever be sorry
because you 've made your choice to stay among poor
folks, and with poor clothes and things, when you might
ha' had everything o' the best."

His sensitiveness on this point had increased as he
10 listened to Eppie's words of faithful affection.

" I can never be sorry, father," said Eppie. " I should n't
know what to think on or to wish for with fine things
about me as I have n't been used to. And it 'ud be
poor work for me to put on things and ride in a gig and
15 sit in a place in church as 'ud make them as I 'm fond of
think me unfitting company for 'em. What could *I* care
for then ? "

Nancy looked at Godfrey with a pained, questioning
glance. But his eyes were fixed on the floor, where he
20 was moving the end of his stick, as if he were pondering
on something absently. She thought there was a word
which might perhaps come better from her lips than from
his.

" What you say is natural, my dear child ; it 's natural
25 you should cling to those who 've brought you up," she
said mildly ; " but there 's a duty you owe to your lawful
father. There 's perhaps something to be given up on
more sides than one. When your father opens his home
to you, I think it 's right you should n't turn your back
30 on it."

" I can't feel as I 've got any father but one," said
Eppie impetuously, while the tears gathered. " I 've
always thought of a little home where he 'd sit i' the
corner, and I should fend and do everything for him. I

can't think o' no other home. I was n't brought up to
be a lady, and I can't turn my mind to it. I like the
working folks and their victuals and their ways. And,"
she ended passionately, while the tears fell, " I promised
to marry a workingman, as 'll live with father and help   5
me to take care of him."

Godfrey looked up at Nancy with a flushed face and
smarting, dilated eyes. This frustration of a purpose
towards which he had set out under the exalted consciousness that he was about to compensate in some degree for 10
the greatest demerit of his life made him feel the air of the
room stifling.

" Let us go," he said, in an undertone.

" We won't talk of this any longer now," said Nancy,
rising. "We 're your wellwishers, my dear, and yours, 15
too, Marner. We shall come and see you again. It 's
getting late now."

In this way she covered her husband's abrupt departure,
for Godfrey had gone straight to the door, unable to say
more.   20

Best

CHAPTER XX.

NANCY and Godfrey walked home under the starlight in silence. When they entered the oaken parlor, Godfrey threw himself into his chair, while Nancy laid down her bonnet and shawl, and stood on the hearth near her hus-5 band, unwilling to leave him even for a few minutes, and yet fearing to utter any word lest it might jar on his feeling. At last Godfrey turned his head towards her, and their eyes met, dwelling in that meeting without any movement on either side. That quiet, mutual gaze of a 10 trusting husband and wife is like the first moment of rest or refuge from a great weariness or a great danger—not to be interfered with by speech or action which would distract the sensations from the fresh enjoyment of repose.

But presently he put out his hand, and as Nancy placed 15 hers within it he drew her towards him, and said :

" That 's ended ! "

She bent to kiss him, and then said, as she stood by his side, " Yes, I 'm afraid we must give up the hope of having her for a daughter. It would n't be right to want to 20 force her to come to us against her will. We can't alter her bringing up and what 's come of it."

" No," said Godfrey, with a keen decisiveness of tone, in contrast with his usually careless and unemphatic speech; " there 's debts we can't pay like money debts, by paying 25 extra for the years that have slipped by. While I 've been putting off and putting off the trees have been growing ; it 's too late now. Marner was in the right in what he said about a man's turning away a blessing from his door : it falls to somebody else. I wanted to pass for childless

once, Nancy ; I shall pass for childless now against my
wish."

Nancy did not speak immediately, but after a little
while she asked, " You won't make it known, then, about
Eppie's being your daughter ? "   5

" No ; where would be the good to anybody ? — only
harm. I must do what I can for her in the state of life she
chooses. I must see who it is she's thinking of marrying."

" If it won't do any good to make the thing known,"
said Nancy, who thought she might now allow herself the 10
relief of entertaining a feeling which she had tried to
silence before, " I should be very thankful for father and
Priscilla never to be troubled with knowing what was done
in the past, more than about Dunsey ; it can't be helped,
— their knowing that."   15

" I shall put it in my will — I think I shall put it in my
will. I should n't like to leave anything to be found out,
like this about Dunsey," said Godfrey meditatively. " But
I can't see anything but difficulties that 'ud come from
telling it now. I must do what I can to make her happy 20
in her own way. I 've a notion," he added, after a moment's pause, " it's Aaron Winthrop she meant she was
engaged to. I remember seeing him with her and Marner
going away from church."

" Well, he 's very sober and industrious," said Nancy, 25
trying to view the matter as cheerfully as possible.

Godfrey fell into thoughtfulness again. Presently he
looked up at Nancy sorrowfully, and said :

" She 's a very pretty, nice girl, is n't she, Nancy ? "

" Yes, dear ; and with just your hair and eyes. I won- 30
dered it had never struck me before."

" I think she took a dislike to me at the thought of my
being her father ; I could see a change in her manner after
that."

"She could n't bear to think of not looking on Marner as her father," said Nancy, not wishing to confirm her husband's painful impression.

"She thinks I did wrong by her mother as well as by her. She thinks me worse than I am. But she *must* think it; she can never know all. It 's part of my punishment, Nancy, for my daughter to dislike me. I should never have got into that trouble if I 'd been true to you — if I had n't been a fool. I 'd no right to expect anything but evil could come of that marriage — and when I shirked doing a father's part, too."

Nancy was silent; her spirit of rectitude would not let her try to soften the edge of what she felt to be a just compunction. He spoke again after a little while, but the tone was rather changed; there was tenderness mingled with the previous self-reproach.

"And I got *you*, Nancy, in spite of all; and yet I 've been grumbling and uneasy because I had n't something else — as if I deserved it."

"You 've never been wanting to me, Godfrey," said Nancy, with quiet sincerity. "My only trouble would be gone if you resigned yourself to the lot that 's been given us."

"Well, perhaps it is n't too late to mend a bit there. Though it *is* too late to mend some things, say what they will."

CHAPTER XXI.

THE next morning, when Silas and Eppie were seated at their breakfast, he said to her :

"Eppie, there's a thing I've had on my mind to do this two year, and now the money's been brought back to us we can do it. I've been turning it over and over in the 5 night, and I think we'll set out to-morrow, while the fine days last. We'll leave the house and everything for your godmother to take care on, and we'll make a little bundle o' things and set out."

"Where to go, daddy?" said Eppie, in much surprise. 10

"To my old country — to the town where I was born — up Lantern Yard. I want to see Mr. Paston, the minister ; something may ha' come out to make 'em know I was innicent o' the robbery. And Mr. Paston was a man with a deal o' light — I want to speak to him about the 15 drawing o' the lots. And I should like to talk to him about the religion o' this countryside, for I partly think he does n't know on it."

Eppie was very joyful, for there was the prospect not only of wonder and delight at seeing a strange country, 20 but also of coming back to tell Aaron all about it. Aaron was so much wiser than she was about most things — it would be rather pleasant to have this little advantage over him. Mrs. Winthrop, though possessed with a dim fear of dangers attendant on so long a journey, and requiring 25 many assurances that it would not take them out of the region of carriers' carts and slow wagons, was nevertheless well pleased that Silas should revisit his own country and find out if he had been cleared from that false accusation.

"You'd be easier in your mind for the rest o' your life, Master Marner," said Dolly ; "that you would. And if there's any light to be got up the yard as you talk on, we've need of it i' this world, and I'd be glad on it myself, if you could bring it back."

So on the fourth day from that time, Silas and Eppie, in their Sunday clothes, with a small bundle tied in a blue linen handkerchief, were making their way through the streets of a great manufacturing town. Silas, bewildered by the changes thirty years had brought over his native place, had stopped several persons in succession to ask them the name of this town, that he might be sure he was not under a mistake about it.

"Ask for Lantern Yard, father ; ask this gentleman with the tassels on his shoulders a-standing at the shop door ; he isn't in a hurry like the rest," said Eppie, in some distress at her father's bewilderment, and ill at ease, besides, amidst the noise, the movement, and the multitude of strange, indifferent faces.

"Eh, my child, he won't know anything about it," said Silas ; "gentlefolks didn't ever go up the Yard. But happen somebody can tell me which is the way to Prison Street, where the jail is. I know the way out o' that as if I'd seen it yesterday."

With some difficulty, after many turnings and new inquiries, they reached Prison Street ; and the grim walls of the jail, the first object that answered to any image in Silas's memory, cheered him with the certitude, which no assurance of the town's name had hitherto given him, that he was in his native place.

"Ah," he said, drawing a long breath, "there's the jail, Eppie ; that's just the same. I aren't afraid now. It's the third turning on the left hand from the jail doors — that's the way we must go."

" Oh, what a dark ugly place ! " said Eppie.   " How it hides the sky !   It 's worse than the workhouse.   I 'm glad you don't live in this town now, father.   Is Lantern Yard like this street ? "

" My precious child," said Silas, smiling, " it is n't a big 5 street like this.   I never was easy i' this street myself, but I was fond o' Lantern Yard.   The shops here are all altered, I think — I can't make 'em out ; but I shall know the turning, because it 's the third."

" Here it is," he said, in a tone of satisfaction, as they 10 came to a narrow alley.   " And then we must go to the left again, and then straight for'ard for a bit, up Shoe Lane ; and then we shall be at the entry next to the o'erhanging window, where there 's the nick in the road for the water to run.   Eh, I can see it all."   15

" O father, I 'm like as if I was stifled," said Eppie.   " I could n't ha' thought as any folks lived i' this way, so close together.   How pretty the Stone-pits 'ull look when we get back ! "

" It looks comical to *me*, child, now — and smells bad. 20 I can't think as it usened to smell so."

Here and there a sallow, begrimed face looked out from a gloomy doorway at the strangers, and increased Eppie's uneasiness, so that it was a longed-for relief when they issued from the alleys into Shoe Lane, where there was a 25 broader strip of sky.

" Dear heart ! " said Silas, " why, there 's people coming out o' the Yard as if they 'd been to chapel at this time o' day — a weekday noon ! "

Suddenly he started and stood still with a look of dis- 30 tressed amazement that alarmed Eppie.   They were before an opening in front of a large factory, from which men and women were streaming for their midday meal.

"Father," said Eppie, clasping his arm, "what's the matter?"

But she had to speak again and again before Silas could answer her.

5 "It's gone, child," he said at last, in strong agitation; "Lantern Yard's gone. It must ha' been here, because here's the house with the o'erhanging window — I know that — it's just the same; but they've made this new opening — and see that big factory! It's all gone —
10 chapel and all."

"Come into that little brush-shop and sit down, father; they'll let you sit down," said Eppie, always on the watch lest one of her father's strange attacks should come on. "Perhaps the people can tell you all about it."

15 But neither from the brush-maker, who had come to Shoe Lane only ten years ago, when the factory was already built, nor from any other source within his reach could Silas learn anything of the old Lantern Yard friends or of Mr. Paston the minister.

20 "The old place is all swep' away," Silas said to Dolly Winthrop on the night of his return, "the little grave-yard and everything. The old home's gone; I've no home but this now. I shall never know whether they got at the truth o' the robbery, nor whether Mr. Paston could
25 ha' given me any light about the drawing o' the lots. It's dark to me, Mrs. Winthrop, that is; I doubt it'll be dark to the last."

"Well, yes, Master Marner," said Dolly, who sat with a placid, listening face, now bordered by gray hairs; "I
30 doubt it may. It's the will o' Them above as a many things should be dark to us; but there's some things as I've never felt i' the dark about, and they're mostly what comes i' the day's work. You were hard done by that once, Master Marner, and it seems as you'll never know

the rights of it; but that does n't hinder there *being* a rights, Master Marner, for all it 's dark to you and me."

"No," said Silas, "no; that does n't hinder. Since the time the child was sent to me and I 've come to love her as myself, I 've had light enough to trusten by; and now she says she 'll never leave me I think I shall trusten till I die."

CONCLUSION.

THERE was one time of the year which was held in Raveloe to be especially suitable for a wedding. It was when
the great lilacs and laburnums in the old-fashioned gardens showed their golden and purple wealth above the
5 lichen-tinted walls, and when there were calves still young
enough to want bucketfuls of fragrant milk. People were
not so busy then as they must become when the full cheese
making and the mowing had set in; and, besides, it was a
time when a light bridal dress could be worn with comfort
10 and seen to advantage.

Happily, the sunshine fell more warmly than usual on
the lilac tufts the morning that Eppie was married, for her
dress was a very light one. She had often thought, though
with a feeling of renunciation, that the perfection of a
15 wedding dress would be a white cotton, with the tiniest
pink sprig at wide intervals; so that when Mrs. Godfrey
Cass begged to provide one, and asked Eppie to choose
what it should be, previous meditation had enabled her to
give a decided answer at once.

20 Seen at a little distance as she walked across the churchyard and down the village, she seemed to be attired in pure
white, and her hair looked like the dash of gold on a lily.
One hand was on her husband's arm, and with the other
she clasped the hand of her father Silas.

25 "You won't be giving me away, father," she had said
before they went to church; "you'll only be taking Aaron
to be a son to you."

Dolly Winthrop walked behind with her husband; and
there ended the little bridal procession.

There were many eyes to look at it, and Miss Priscilla Lammeter was glad that she and her father had happened to drive up to the door of the Red House just in time to see this pretty sight. They had come to keep Nancy company to-day, because Mr. Cass had had to go away to Lytherley, for special reasons. That seemed to be a pity, for otherwise he might have gone, as Mr. Crackenthorp and Mr. Osgood certainly would, to look on at the wedding feast which he had ordered at the Rainbow, naturally feeling a great interest in the weaver who had been wronged by one of his own family.

"I could ha' wished Nancy had had the luck to find a child like that and bring her up," said Priscilla to her father, as they sat in the gig; "I should ha' had something young to think of then, besides the lambs and the calves."

"Yes, my dear, yes," said Mr. Lammeter; "one feels that as one gets older. Things look dim to old folks; they'd need have some young eyes about 'em, to let 'em know the world's the same as it used to be."

Nancy came out now to welcome her father and sister; and the wedding group had passed on beyond the Red House to the humbler part of the village.

Dolly Winthrop was the first to divine that old Mr. Macey, who had been set in his armchair outside his own door, would expect some special notice as they passed, since he was too old to be at the wedding feast.

"Mr. Macey's looking for a word from us," said Dolly; "he'll be hurt if we pass him and say nothing — and him so racked with rheumatiz."

So they turned aside to shake hands with the old man. He had looked forward to the occasion, and had his premeditated speech.

"Well, Master Marner," he said, in a voice that qua-

vered a good deal, " I 've lived to see my words come true.
I was the first to say there was no harm in you, though
your looks might be again' you ; and I was the first to say
you 'd get your money back.　And it 's nothing but right-
5　ful as you should.　And I 'd ha' said the ' Amens,' and
willing, at the holy matrimony; but Tookey 's done it a
good while now, and I hope you 'll have none the worse
luck."

In the open yard before the Rainbow the party of
10　guests were already assembled, though it was still nearly
an hour before the appointed feast time.　But by this
means they could not only enjoy the slow advent of their
pleasure ; they had also ample leisure to talk of Silas
Marner's strange history, and arrive by due degrees at
15　the conclusion that he had brought a blessing on himself
by acting like a father to a lone, motherless child.　Even
the farrier did not negative this sentiment ; on the contrary, he took it up as peculiarly his own, and invited any
hardy person present to contradict him.　But he met
20　with no contradiction ; and all differences among the
company were merged in a general agreement with Mr.
Snell's sentiment, that when a man had deserved his
good luck it was the part of his neighbors to wish him
joy.

25　　As the bridal group approached, a hearty cheer was
raised in the Rainbow yard ; and Ben Winthrop, whose
jokes had retained their acceptable flavor, found it agreeable to turn in there and receive congratulations, not
requiring the proposed interval of quiet at the Stone-pits
30　before joining the company.

Eppie had a larger garden than she had ever expected
there now ; and in other ways there had been alterations
at the expense of Mr. Cass, the landlord, to suit Silas's
larger family.　For he and Eppie had declared that they

would rather stay at the Stone-pits than go to any new home.   The garden was fenced with stones on two sides, but in front there was an open fence, through which the flowers shone with answering gladness, as the four united people came within sight of them.   5

   " O father," said Eppie, "what a pretty home ours is ! I think nobody could be happier than we are."

NOTES.

Chapter I.

What end does the double title serve? What rules should govern the choice of titles? See Genung's *Practical Rhetoric*, pp. 258–260.

1 1. **In the days,** etc. — **Far-off time.** What artistic reason for giving the time by these phrases instead of in exact years?

1 10. **Winter sunset.** Why is *winter* sunset chosen?

Begin to note the vast number of words of Latin origin. Substitute equivalents of Anglo-Saxon if possible. How would the use of these words change the style? Genung, *P. R.*, pp. 43, 44.

1 27. Find five pure English words in the first paragraph.

Is this a good introductory paragraph? Why? Genung, *P. R.*, pp. 267–272.

1 28. What words mark the transition from paragraph 1 to paragraph 2?

3 21. **Speak fair:** treat deferentially.

3 23. **Demon-worship.** What is the meaning of demon here in distinction from our common usage?

3 25. **For the rude mind.** How is a man's conception of God shaped by his everyday experience?

3 32. **Illuminated by religious faith.** Who were some of the preachers at that time who brought religious enthusiasm to English working classes? See Green's *English History*, Chap. X, Sec. 1, for an account of the Wesleys.

Read description of Dinah's preaching in *Adam Bede*, Chap. II.

4 4. **I.** Notice the introduction of personal element. Effect of this?

4 9. Notice how the *theme* of this second paragraph is expanded by definition, explanation, repetition, and incident. Distinguish each. Genung, *P. R.*, pp. 249–260.

4 10. Note the logical sequence of these two paragraphs, — the first being general or class description; the second, specific or individual.

4 10. Why begin paragraph 3 with "and"?

Raveloe. Evidently a place well known to George Eliot ; a fertile spot, perhaps near her early home in Warwickshire.

4 25. **Lifting more imposing fronts,** etc. What idea of the character of inhabitants is at once given by this?

4 33. **War times.** Refers to war with France, lasting from 1793 to Waterloo in 1815. Living expenses at that time were enormous.

4 34. **Christmas, Whitsuntide,** etc. The three great church festivals. Note the old English " tide " for " time."

4 34. Is this picture of Raveloe presented to the reader by detail or by impression?

5 1. The place and character have been described; now follows an exposition of their relation to each other.

5 2. **Pallid.** How does the *second* use of this word link Silas to his class?

5 11. **Rainbow:** village inn.

5 32. **More by token:** "and also " — "moreover." Notice how Mr. Macey's argument accords with his character and position in town. What appeals to him most strongly is that a stroke "throws a man on the parish."

6 25. **Speak fair.** How was this phrase used before? Significance of using it now in connection with Silas. See 3 21.

7 12. **Fine sight of money.** Note introduction of a new element, — an added interest in Silas brought in at the right moment.

7 15. **But.** Notice change of thought introduced by the adversative conjunction.

7 23. **Artisan.** How different in meaning from artist or workman?

Narrow religious sect. At that time there were springing up in England numerous independent churches ; the members of these churches, on account of their separation from the Established Church, were called Dissenters.

8 10. **A less truthful man,** etc. Examine carefully the thought, expression, and form of this sentence. Note the antithesis and parallel expressions. What philosophic truth in the last part?

8 30. **David and Jonathan.** Read I Sam. xviii.

9 6. **The expression,** etc. Note the heightened effect produced by contrast. See Macaulay's *Essay on Milton,* paragraph beginning "The Puritans were men whose minds," for one of the finest contrasts in English language.

9 22. **Whose unnurtured souls,** etc. Explain simile.

9 24. Now the narrative fairly begins. Notice how swiftly it moves up to the point of Marner's examination. Reason for this?

11 25. Why does George Eliot give a full description of the examination?

12 20. **Give Satan advantage.** Note the Biblical phraseology used by these people.

12 21. **Suddenly a deep flush.** Note dramatic effect.

13 5. **Drawing lots.** A custom based upon Biblical authority.

13 11. **His trust in man cruelly bruised.** Here we have the first great change in Marner's character.

13 24. **There is no just God.** This shows the depth of the change.

14 14. **If there is an angel,** etc. Mark as one of the truest and most happily expressed sentiments of George Eliot.

Note the completeness, clearness, vividness of the condensed narration of Silas's early life. Genung, *P. R.*, pp. 363-368.

QUESTIONS FOR END OF CHAPTER I.

1. Criticise this as an introductory chapter. How are the questions when? and who? answered?

2. Note the perfect transitions from one paragraph to another. Marked by what words in each case? Note the logical sequence of paragraphs: cause before effect and general before particular. Genung, *P. R.*, p. 263, Art. 2.

3. Examine carefully description of Raveloe and Silas; observe the combination of the pure narrative (pp. 18-23); the dramatic (pp. 20-22); and the analytical or reflective writing (p. 13 and the last paragraph).

4. Why is it more artistic to place Silas in Raveloe first and then work backwards than to work from his life in Lantern Yard up to his residence at Raveloe?

5. What new ideas of the personality of George Eliot do you get from this one chapter?

CHAPTER II.

See study of transitional paragraph, Genung, *P. R.*, pp. 212, 213.

15 1. How is the transition made in the beginning of this chapter from one place to another? Is change in place the only distinction between the spirit of this chapter and the preceding one?

Notice the perfect picture of English country scenery in paragraph 1.

15 26. **The whitewashed walls,** etc. A good picture of worship among the Dissenters.

16 15. Notice the contrast between the plenty at Raveloe and the poverty at Lantern Yard.

What is the psychological truth in paragraph 3?

18 30. Note how the love of money for its own sake comes unconsciously to Marner. He is not a miser from choice.

18 32. Mark the pathos in the incident of Sally Oates.

20 14. **Brought silver:** "cross the palm with silver." A phrase originating in the practice of paying silver to gypsies for telling fortunes. The old English penny had a cross upon it. In *As You Like It*, Touchstone says to Rosalind: "For my part, I would rather bear with you than bear you: yet I should bear no cross, if I did bear you, for I think you have no money in your purse."

22 6. **Flock beds:** beds filled with wool. What is the derivation of the word "flock"?

22 13. Notice here that an affectionate nature thwarted in one direction must burst out in another. Marner had lost faith in man; his hoard of money takes man's place, and, as a human, understanding friend, he loves it. Other men might spend themselves on literary or scientific research. Simple, unlearned Marner took the tangible money which happened to come into his life. What did Bunyan do under similar circumstances?

Note passages in this chapter where the psychological development of Marner's character is portrayed by analysis and where by descriptive pictures. Could any careful analysis have given us the information that is in the paragraph beginning, "So, year after year"? Notice how the last transitional paragraph prepares the way for the coming chapter.

CHAPTER III.

25 1. Notice the quick change in scene and tone. What principle of contrast here illustrated? Genung, *P. R.*, p. 103. Dickens excels in contrast of characters and scenes.

25 16. **Yeoman:** independent farmer.

25 21. **Currents of industrial energy.** As seen at the manufactories of Birmingham and Manchester.

27 2. **Wainscot.** What is gained by use of metonomy here? Genung, *P. R.*, p. 88.

28 34. **Elders and betters.** From the Catechism.

What is the moral weakness of each brother? Godfrey, having the finer sensibilities, suffers more acutely.

34 18. **Cats and dogs.** There was a Teutonic myth which said that cats influenced the rain and dogs the wind.

34 25. **Crooked sixpence.** For luck.

In paragraph beginning, " With that Dunstan," etc., note George Eliot's sympathetic understanding of the way in which men bind themselves by the fetters of sin and indiscretion ; in the next paragraph note the influence of surroundings on character ; and in the next how "conscience doth make cowards of us all."

37 14. **Strong silken rope.** See Richard Watson Gilder's " Love is not bond to any man."

38 32. **Perhaps because she saw no other career open to her.** Bring out the thought by emphasis on "she."

Notice that George Eliot's interest is always in development of character ; therefore, she spends the greater part of this chapter on the analysis of Godfrey Cass's nature.

CHAPTER IV.

Study Genung, *P. R.*, on Incident, p. 296.

Notice in this chapter how the temptation grows upon Dunstan.

46 10. **Who would know ?** Why is this sentence italicized ?

Notice the incidents of the horse trading, the run, the gold-handled whip, the backward route home. How do these describe the character of Dunstan ? Note the vividness of delineation by incident. Do circumstances in real life aid men in carrying out their criminal impulses ?

CHAPTER V.

In this chapter George Eliot takes up the thread of events which happened simultaneously with those of the preceding chapter. Genung, *P. R.*, pp. 371–5.

48 5. **Horn lantern.** A large horn was scraped thin and a candle placed inside ; originally spelt lant-horn.

48 10. Why is the present tense used in the third sentence? Genung, *P. R.*, p. 113, Art. 6.

48 10. **The lapse of time,** etc. Illustrate this truth from your own experience.

49 7. Why is Marner made to look forward so intensely to the enjoyment of his gold?

50 4. **So as to merge.** Notice here a detail which the writer must supply to make the disappearance of the money more mysterious. Is the expression misleading?

50 33. **He rose.** Notice the climax of the description following.

Trace the different impulses of Marner after the discovery of his loss. Where is the *real* pathos of his loss?

54 1. **Hectoring.** Hector, the Trojan leader. See *Iliad*, Bk. XXII.

Chapter VI.

55 2. **Rainbow.** Inns were first marked by signs in the days when reading was not a common accomplishment.

58 3. **Basson, key bugle.** This was before the days of organs.

64 2. **Queen's head went out.** Shillings made in Queen Anne's day and stamped with the royal head.

In this chapter we have a good example of George Eliot's knowledge of all sides of life. How could she know anything about such a group of country people?

Note the accuracy of George Eliot's dialect, her strong sense of humor, and her knowledge of technical terms. This is an ideal portrayal of a typical village inn gathering.

For study of Dialect in Narrative, see Genung, *P. R.*, pp. 82, 83.

Chapter VII.

68 4. Notice the two contrasts: one between Marner and the men at the inn; the other, between the cold outside and the warmth inside.

68 7. **Like antennæ.** Criticise the simile.

68 26. Trace the change from fear to curiosity as Marner tells of his troubles.

69 26. **Information to lay.** *I.e.*, before a court.

72 8. Compare the accusation against Jim Rodney and that against Silas at Lantern Yard. Would that account for Silas's saying, "I don't accuse you, I won't accuse anybody"?

70 30. **Our consciousness,** etc. Consider the truth of this statement. This is the beginning of Silas's return to faith in his fellow-men.

73 15. **Nolo episcopari:** "I do not wish to be bishop." A formal protestation made at the consecration by the candidate for the bishopric.

What sentence contains the central thought of this chapter?

Chapter VIII.

75 14. Notice the humor in depicting the growth of suspicion against the peddler.

78 9. **A well-intentioned person,** etc. Observe how completely the character is drawn in three phrases.

82 20. What new light is thrown on the character of Godfrey Cass in his plan for confessing to his father?

83 14. We have here a good example of the way in which one concession to weakness hampers a man in every action throughout life. Godfrey's early indiscretion compromised him always.

What characteristics of the father had passed by heredity to the son?

Does the careful analysis in this chapter retard the narrative? See Genung, *P. R.*, pp. 364–6.

Chapter IX.

90 23. **Shilly-shally.** Derived from will I, shall I?

Does the moral teaching of this chapter seem obtrusive?

What particulars increase respect for Godfrey, and what increase contempt for him?

Chapter X.

94 5. **Commission of peace:** a board appointed by the king.

95 25. **Wall-eyed.** The origin of this phrase is interesting.

95 28. **Mere skimming dishes.** Value of this figure?

The first two paragraphs give the current feelings of opinionists on each side, and then the story is carried back to Silas again.

The third paragraph by contrast and repetition shows us the intensity of Marner's grief.

97 3. **Not utterly forsaken.** Why are the neighbors so interested in Silas? Does it not compare with the newspaper reporters' interest of to-day?

97 17. **Black puddings:** sausages.

98 17. What is Mr. Macey's philosophy of life?

101 14. **So eager for duties.** An acute characterization.

102 30. **Faint consciousness.** The bringing back of Silas to a dependency on his fellow-men has already begun.

103 29. **I. H. S. :** originally the first three letters of the Greek word for Jesus, — ΙΗΣΟΥΣ. Now usually explained as the initials for Jesu Hominum Salvator.

104 26. **There have been no bells.** What is the effect of the sentence brought in here ?

106 12. Difference between theology and religion ?

107 21. George Eliot shows by her picture of little Aaron that she understands child nature perfectly.

107 31. **God rest you :** a famous English carol.

108 7. **Erol :** herald ; English country fashion of dropping the h.

What is the contrast between Dolly's and Mr. Macey's methods of consolation ?

110 3. **Athanasian creed.** Formulated according to the principles of Athanasius, Bishop of Alexandria in the fourth century. An epitome of the Orthodox faith.

Notice the contrast between the surroundings of Silas and the Cass family, and yet the similarity between the anxieties of Silas and Godfrey.

CHAPTER XI.

113 2. **A joseph :** a riding habit, somewhat like a man's overcoat, buttoned plainly down the front.

115 5. **Direct proportion.** Exact meaning of this mathematical term ?

The contrast between the Misses Gunn and Nancy is especially skillful. Its object, of course, is to enhance the virtues, beauty, and sweet good sense of Nancy.

118 22. Meaning of " profane literature " ?

119 6. **Blowzy :** red from the wind. This word occurs in Goldsmith's *Vicar of Wakefield* and in Tennyson's *Princess*.

Why is Priscilla attractive? She, too, serves as a foil for Nancy.

129 29. **Sir Roger de Coverley :** an old-fashioned English dance, taking its name from Sir Roger of the *Spectator*.

Observe the picture made by the procession from the dining-room to the parlor.

131 12. **Take tithe in kind :** to receive pay in farmers' produce.

In this chapter George Eliot again is at her best in delineation of types of character. Her men and women are living beings, and she understands them as they could not understand themselves. Nancy's treatment of Godfrey is delightfully true to life ; also her circumscribed notions of faithfulness to principles.

Does not the good cheer and happiness of this chapter foreshadow some catastrophe which is to break Godfrey's dream?

Chapter XII.

Notice the skillful contrast in the opening paragraph.

139 14. **But the complete torpor came.** This paragraph is a masterpiece of contrast and unexpected climax.

141 21. **When Marner's sensibility returned,** etc. From the first we see the influence that the child is to have on Marner. The gold curls to replace the lost gold is a pretty fancy.

This chapter is one of the best in the book. It is full of a dramatic power which the author could not resist. Compare her treatment with that which such dramatic events might receive from a sensational writer.

Chapter XIII.

145 1. Mark the easy, direct return to the Red House.

145 10. Kimble is a type of many card players.

146 17. Consider the effectiveness of bringing Marner and the child into the Squire's party.

151 20. **At the end of sixteen years.** Is it artistic to anticipate what is coming?

153 30. Examine and judge the philosophy of the last paragraph.

Is Godfrey's action in this chapter consistent with his character as first drawn for us?

Chapter XIV.

155 1. The chapter opens with a model introductory paragraph, finishing up what was left incomplete in the last chapter and starting a new line of thought.

157 7. **Scrat and fend :** seek to provide.

157 12. **Moithered :** puzzled.

157 15. **The clock seems to stand still.** A key to Dolly's character.

158 15. The comparison in Silas's mind between Eppie and the gold is beautiful, and shows the awakening of the man's soul.

164 20. **Goliath.** See I Samuel xvii. Here the individual name is generalized by the article to denote a whole class.

164 27. We have here a charming picture of irrepressible childhood, and perplexed outwitted inexperience.

169 9. **No child was afraid.** Showing most effectually the change that had come to Silas.

170 5. Analyze the beauty of the last paragraph of the chapter. Is it wholly beauty of thought, or yet wholly beauty of expression?

The psychology of the reciprocal influence of Silas and Eppie is perfect, and is beautifully told.

Chapter XV.

What is the effect of the irony used in this chapter? See Genung, *P. R.*, p. 100.

What is the difference between irony and sarcasm, and which could be legitimately used here?

What must be the reader's feeling toward Godfrey's weakness?

Notice that Part I ends with general happiness and contentment.

All the important elements of the story have been presented. In Part II we see the results of the actions which have taken place upon the different characters.

172 16. Note the suggestiveness of the last sentence of Part I.

Chapter XVI.

173 6. **Richer parishioners.** Notice the truth of this half-sarcastic observation.

173 13. Notice the happy atmosphere given by the first paragraph.

173 26. **To all who love human faces best.** Here is given us the reason why faces of those we know best are the most interesting and dearest to us.

174 23. To what is the change in Godfrey and Nancy due?

174 30. The contrast between Silas and Eppie is very effective. She seems to belong much more to Godfrey and Nancy.

177 8. **Mr. Cass has been so good to us.** Godfrey's reparation.

178 13. The donkey, dog, and kitten all give an air of domestic happiness.

180 2. **Gods of the hearth:** Lares and Penates, bringers of health and wealth to the household.

181 19. Silas's natural return to community life has made possible the recital of the story which he had so long been forced to keep locked in his heart.

183 16. **I've often a deal inside of me.** Mrs. Winthrop's own analysis of her character.

183 26. To follow Mrs. Winthrop's philosophy of life and religion is one of the most interesting problems of the book. There is rare beauty of faith and hope in the plain woman.

191 2. The pathetic suggestion of the pipe going out gives the needed final touch to this scene.

Chapter XVII.

192 1. The opening paragraph of this chapter gives us a better idea of the wife Nancy than any description of her could do.

193 29. **Turned.** As soon as Michaelmas comes, 29th of September.

194 5. There is a difference between the practicality of Priscilla and that of Nancy. What is it ?

195 6. **Disappointed at not having any children.** The one lack in their lives ; the natural substitute is at once suggested and the writing of Part II justified.

196 4. **Mant's Bible :** an annotated edition by Bishop Mant.

198 21. **It was as necessary to her mind.** In strong contrast to Godfrey's mind.

This whole chapter is a skillful summary of the past disappointment in the lives of Godfrey and Nancy, and the best preparation in way of suspense for what is to follow.

Chapter XVIII.

206 8. **Seals.** These were necessary articles before the art of writing had become general.

In this scene we see again vividly how much broader is Nancy's nature than Godfrey's, even while he is ennobling himself by the confession of his fault. His nature at its greatest could not compass the generosity of hers, or he would not have anticipated bitterness and reproach from her.

Chapter XIX.

210 8. **It had only reached the stage.** A clear analysis of an almost indefinable sensation.

215 32. **Godfrey felt an irritation.** It seems as if even the poor reparation he could make was denied him.

216 17. **Then, sir.** The long slumbering spirit in Marner at last awakened.

Chapter XX.

This last glimpse of Godfrey and Nancy is fully satisfying.

Chapter XXI.

225 3. **There's one thing I've had on my mind.** The only trouble left to Marner.

228 20. The disappearance of Lantern Yard separates Silas completely from his old life.

Conclusion.

The ending of the story is bright and happy, with the exception of the little shadow which still rests on Godfrey and Nancy. It is only George Eliot's theory of life: that those who struggle nobly and live honorable lives do obtain final happiness; but those who have erred can never quite escape the cloud of their transgression.

SPECIAL STUDY OF SILAS MARNER.

SUBJECT–MATTER.

PRINCIPLE to be remembered here is that George Eliot's peculiar interest is in *man* as *man* and the possibility of individual development under given conditions of heredity and environment. Her text is : " Be ye perfect even as I am perfect," and her motto : " I cannot stir a step aside from what I believe to be true in character."

1. From what classes of society are the characters in *Silas Marner* chosen ? How do these two classes serve as foils to each other ? What artistic aim in this choice ?

2. Who are the principal characters ? According to what principle is the division between principal and subordinate characters made ?

3. Which two characters are most carefully developed ?

4. Which one character is more carefully developed ? Justify title of book.

5. Who are the secondary characters, and what part do they play ? What is the value of secondary characters in general ? Compare the ratio between importance given to secondary characters and that given to principal characters in the works of George Eliot, Thackeray, Dickens. Has the standard of this ratio changed in modern fiction, generally speaking ?

6. Where are the two best *groups* of characters in the book ? Which is the portrayal of feminine weakness, and which of masculine ? Which is executed best ? Any reason for this ?

7. Who is the real heroine of the book ? On what principle do you base your answer ?

8. Criticise her portrayal of the children. (See "George Eliot's Children," *Macmillan's Magazine*, October, 1882.)

Compare these children with the children of Dickens and Thackeray. Is there anything in George Eliot's life which accounts for her conception of childhood?

9. Character of Silas Marner:

    a. Trace the changes in his character from beginning to end, accounting for each.

    b. Study carefully the influence of Eppie. Is there any special artistic fitness in having Eppie the child of Godfrey Cass?

    c. What little event at the end of the book *completes* the change in the character of Silas?

10. How and by what means are the characters of Godfrey and Nancy Cass developed?

11. Is there any character in the book which does not develop? Compare characters of Dickens and Thackeray in this respect.

12. What is George Eliot's attitude towards all her characters? Is there one in *Silas Marner* that excites contempt and disgust more than pity? Read *Sidney Lanier*, chapter on George Eliot.

13. What is the character of George Eliot's humor? Is there ever any bitterness in it? Compare with Dickens and Thackeray in this respect.

14. What is the quality of the pathos of *Silas Marner?* Is it pathos of thought or of expression, or of both? In what does the pathos of the *whole* sketch lie?

15. Examine book entitled *Wit and Wisdom of George Eliot.* Make your own selections (ten) from *Silas Marner.*

16. What is Mrs. Winthrop's philosophy of life? Her place in the story?

STRUCTURE.

I. PLAN OF THE NARRATIVE.

1. Analyze the book according to chapters.
2. Into what two parts does the book naturally divide itself?
3. What is the *subject* of the book? ⎫ Genung, *Practical*
4. What is the theme of the book? ⎭ *Rhetoric,* pp. 249–260.

5. How many different threads of the story are there?

6. Are these threads carried along parallel or do they cross?

7. Is there in any chapter undue anticipation of what is to follow? What rule should the sequence of chapters follow? Genung, *P. R.*, p. 263.

8. What part is played by the great stone pit? Compare with river in *Mill on the Floss*.

9. Are characters and incidents unduly crowded into certain chapters, or is there equal distribution of the whole?

10. Is there any superfluous chapter? Could any paragraph be cut out without loss? Discuss the economy of the book.

11. Take your analysis by chapters and consider it as the mere skeleton in George Eliot's mind. How does she dress the skeleton? Select the best character description; the best nature description; most poetical passage; the expression of loftiest thought; best humor; tenderest pathos.

12. Is the ending of the work artistic? Reason for answer. Genung, *P. R.*, pp. 280–282.

13. What questions should a narrative answer? Test *Silas Marner* by these rules.

14. See Wendell's *English Composition* or Genung's *Practical Rhetoric*, Rules for Unity, Mass, Coherence.

Test the structure of *Silas Marner* by these rules.

Test the structure of the chapters, taken separately, by these rules.

II. MATERIALS OF THE STORY.

1. An author draws his material from two separate sources : first, the world of nature ; second, the world of man.

2. Give five instances where George Eliot draws her material from the world of nature.

3. From the world of man, what institutions of church, society, industry, superstition, and tradition are used?

4. Which attributes of human character has George Eliot pictured most strongly? Does she give the larger place to hate and revenge or to love and moral courage?

III. Setting.

1. The setting of a story is the statement of the locality and time in which the events portrayed took place.

2. Is the setting of *Silas Marner* given definitely, or is it to be inferred from certain allusions to historical facts and characters? History and biography necessarily use the definite setting; fiction and poetry give the setting usually by allusion. For example, the presence of the Crusaders, Prince John, and King Richard gives the setting of *Ivanhoe*. How is the time given by allusion in the *Vision of Sir Launfal?* In Landor's *Imaginary Conversations* the setting is never formally given, but is inferred from apparently casual suggestions. See *Hannibal and Marcellus,* or *Henry VIII and Anne Boleyn.*

IV. Plot.

1. The writer begins with the plot from within and works outward; the reader works from the outside in towards the plot.

2. In *Silas Marner*, is the reader first attracted to the plot by an incident or a character?

3. Write out the plot in a hundred words, following the rule that the plot is the chain of those incidents only which are indispensable to the story.

4. Does the plot conform to the requirements of consistency, interest, relief, and climax?

5. From what one character in *Silas Marner* does the plot take its unity?

6. What is the dramatic climax of the book?

V. Incidents

1. The incidents which are indispensable to the thread of the story are called plot incidents; those that lead up to the plot incidents, developing incidents.

2. Of which kind must there be the greater number in any novel? Cite two of each class in *Silas Marner.*

3. The purpose of the developing incidents may be to portray character, afford relief, or reflect the movement of the story. Cite one of each purpose in *Silas Marner.*

4. A plot incident with its developing incidents forms an episode. Give two episodes in the narrative of *Silas Marner.*

VI. CHARACTER.

1. Study the characters of Silas, Godfrey, and Nancy Cass in the light of heredity, innate tendencies, environment, development, dominant motive, and accomplishments in life.

STYLE.

I. EXPRESSION OR DICTION.

NOTE. 1. Paragraphing — special attention to transition and massing.

2. Sentence formation.
3. Choice of words.
4. Rhetorical figures.
5. Nobility, grace, and delicacy of expression.
6. Allusion.
7. Rhythm.
8. Sincerity of style.
9. Energy of style.
10. Logical force.
11. Individuality of style.

II. METHOD.

1. Is the author's narrative straightforward?

2. Is the proportion of narrative and description good? Genung, *P. R.*, p. 369.

3. Does the author comment upon the characters or let them speak entirely for themselves?

4. Is the life portrayed real or ideal?

5. Is the author's canvas large or small?

6. Is there enough allusion to give a literary atmosphere to the book?

7. Is George Eliot's greatest strength in handling plot, depicting character, or giving dramatic situations?

III. PURPOSE.

1. Is the author's purpose artistic, to set forth a historical picture, to give her own philosophic views, or simply to entertain?

SUBJECTS FOR PAPERS.

    I. "Habit is ten times Nature."
    II. How Eppie changed the Character of Marner.
   III. The Philosophy of Mrs. Winthrop.
   IV. The Company at the Rainbow.
    V. The Great Stone Pit.
   VI. Development of Godfrey and Nancy Cass.
  VII. How George Eliot treats Life.
 VIII. Wit and Wisdom of *Silas Marner*.
   IX. A Book Review of *Silas Marner*.

ADVERTISEMENTS

STANDARD ENGLISH CLASSICS

EDITED BY COMPETENT SCHOLARS WITH SPECIAL REFERENCE
TO COLLEGE REQUIREMENTS.

Tennyson's The Princess. Edited by ALBERT S. COOK, Professor of English Literature in Yale University. 40 cents.

Carlyle's Essay on Burns. Edited by CHARLES L. HANSON, Teacher of English in the B. M. C. Durfee High School, Fall River, Mass. 30 cents.

Macaulay's Essay on Milton. Edited by HERBERT A. SMITH, Instructor in English in Yale University. 25 cents.

Macaulay's Essay on Addison. Edited by HERBERT A. SMITH. 35 cents.

Macaulay's Essays on Addison and Milton. (In one volume.) Edited by HERBERT A. SMITH. 50 cents.

Dryden's Palamon and Arcite. Edited by GEORGE E. ELIOT, Jr., Instructor in English in Morgan School, Clinton, Conn. 35 cents.

George Eliot's Silas Marner. Edited by R. ADELAIDE WITHAM, Teacher of English in Latin High School, Somerville, Mass. 50 cents.

Sir Roger de Coverley Papers. From "*The Spectator.*" Edited by MARY E. LITCHFIELD. cents.

Coleridge's Ancient Mariner. Edited by L. R. GIBBS. 25 cents.

Pope's Translation of the Iliad. *Books I., VI., XXII., and XXIV.* Edited by WILLIAM TAPPAN. 35 cents.

Macaulay's Lays of Ancient Rome. Edited by M. GRANT DANIELL, recently Principal of Chauncy-Hall School. cents.

Cooper's Last of the Mohicans. Edited by JOHN B. DUNBAR, Instructor in English in the Boys' High School, Brooklyn, N. Y. cents.

Shakespeare's Macbeth. Edited by Rev. HENRY N. HUDSON. 35 cents.

Burke's Speech on Conciliation with America. Edited by HAMMOND LAMONT, Associate Professor of Rhetoric in Brown University. 40 cents.

Goldsmith's Vicar of Wakefield. Edited by D. H. MONTGOMERY. 40 cents.

Edmund Burke's Letter to a Noble Lord. Edited by ALBERT H. SMYTH, Professor of English Literature in the Central High School, Philadelphia. 30 cents.

Selections from Irving's Sketch Book. Edited, with Introduction and Notes, by MARY E. LITCHFIELD. cents.

De Quincey's Revolt of the Tartars. Edited by W. E. SIMONDS, Professor of English Literature in Knox College, Galesburg, Ill. cents.

Milton's Paradise Lost, Books I. and II., and Lycidas. Edited by HOMER B. SPRAGUE. 40 cents.

GINN & COMPANY, Publishers,

Boston.   New York.   Chicago.   Atlanta.   Dallas.

BOOKS ON ENGLISH LITERATURE

GINN & COMPANY, Publishers,

Boston.   New York.   Chicago.   Atlanta.   Dallas.